DAVID WHITE, CRIME REPORTER

☆☆☆

David White

CRIME REPORTER

by Milton Lewis

1958   New York

DODD, MEAD & COMPANY

TO my dear wife, Mildred Brown Lewis, without whom this book could not have been written, and who, in fact, should be listed as co-author. Instead, I can only offer her my love —and royalties.

☆☆☆

FOREWORD

Milt Lewis is a top crime reporter on the New York *Herald Tribune*. He has covered many different, important and exciting stories, including the Adam Clayton Powell income tax evasion case, the Mad Bomber, the Judith Coplon espionage case, the acid blinding of Victor Riesel and the Anastasia murder.

As a continuing assignment, Mr. Lewis is concerned with the tentacles of the "Invisible Government." Repeated summit conferences of the crime syndicates—the most recent at Apalachin—have caused the Justice Department to establish a special division to tackle this major problem.

If our homes, businesses and communities are to be safe from the machinations of the racketeers and the operations of the local syndicate, much will depend on the initiative of the crime reporter. His is a dangerous and sometimes grueling assignment. It involves the checking of many facts, the running down of numerous false leads and the ultimate putting together of the pattern that spells crime in our town and corruption in high office. This can result—and often does—in indictments and public action.

I am delighted Milt Lewis has written this story of a crime reporter and his subsequent progress in the newspaper profession. It gives a behind-the-scenes picture that is accurate, vivid and interesting. And it may lead others to enter this very rewarding and important career.

OGDEN R. REID, Editor
New York *Herald Tribune*

CONTENTS

DAVID WHITE, CRIME REPORTER

HIS FIRST ASSIGNMENT

IT WAS A SNOWY NIGHT in March, and, as on most Sunday nights, things were extremely quiet at the morning *Ledger*. The first edition was already in, and the presses would roll in about five minutes.

David White, who had been running copy on the paper since late June, regarded the scene with satisfaction. He had come to know the routine in the city room quite well—a room half the size of a football field and dominated by E. E. Holloway, the city editor.

A big bear of a man, Holly was a never-ending source of surprise and respect to David. He could be gentle as a child and snappish as a lion, as the occasion demanded. But he was extremely fair—and about as shrewd as they came. Just the other day, for instance, Holly had summoned a young reporter to the city desk and congratulated him on having turned in a crisp, fast-moving story.

The young man was visibly swelling with pleasure when Holly tossed in an after-thought. "By the way," he said dryly, "there is no such thing as a 'new innovation.' Let's not be redundant, eh?"

Right now, Holly was reaching for the tie he habitually tossed into a lower drawer as soon as he came to work.

"It may not look exactly dignified," he once explained, "but I find I work better without wearing a tie, just as I could never wear a jacket in the office. They bind me."

It was his custom, as David knew, to wait for the first edition to come up from the pressroom and scan it to see how the stories were laid out—especially on page one and the first page of the second section, known as the "split page" or the "second front."

Normally, the first edition of the *Ledger's* chief rival, the *Transcript,* printed about a mile away and with similar deadlines, would be brought in as Holloway was looking at his own newspaper. He would go through "The Opposition," to see if it had something significant the *Ledger* might have missed in its own coverage. If not, he would slip into his jacket and coat, bid his assistants on the city desk good night and leave.

From the expression on Holly's face, David could see that "The Opposition" seemed to have nothing special tonight. The desk men, who were also watching their editor closely, relaxed.

Holloway stood up, stretched his big frame and reached for the jacket he had tossed casually over the back of his chair some ten hours previously.

He had just slipped an arm into a sleeve when one of the three phones on the desk rang. It was answered by James Bryan, the assistant night city editor, with his usual—"City Desk, Bryan." His next words electrified the room.

"What's that? O.K., O.K. We'll do what we can from this end. Call back as soon as possible—and don't forget the passenger list!"

Passenger list!

With those words, Holloway tossed his jacket back on the chair and pulled his tie off, even as Bryan blurted:

"That was Miller, at Jackson Airport. Plane crash. Forty aboard. Happened on take-off. Plane on fire—all believed dead. Headed for Chicago and Los Angeles."

David sprinted for the wire service ticker, which was beginning to clatter. A bell on the ticker also began clanging, indicating a bulletin was coming.

Holloway looked about at his almost empty city room. It couldn't have happened at a worse time.

The only ones present were four rewrite men and two general assignment reporters, who were working on special features for later in the week. Well, they could be pulled off that easily enough. But only these two were immediately available. And here was the best story of the night coming up. At least half the passengers on that plane might well be New Yorkers. There was no telling the number of fairly prominent people aboard. And the first report: all dead.

The wire service ticker ceased its clattering for a moment and David ripped off the sheet and rushed it over to Holloway:

POLICE REPORT THAT A WORLD WIDE SUPERLINER BOUND FOR CHICAGO AND LOS ANGELES CRASHED ON TAKE OFF FROM JACKSON FIELD. AMBULANCES FROM SIX HOSPITALS ARE BE- ING RUSHED TO THE SCENE ALONG WITH POLICE DISASTER UNITS. UNOFFICIAL REPORTS STATE THERE WERE ABOUT FORTY PERSONS ABOARD. ALL ARE BELIEVED DEAD. MORE LATER.

Holloway took command quickly.

"Flash the east and west side district men and move them out to the airport to assist Miller," he told Bryan. "Tell them, if they've got any sense, to stay away from cabs—the Sunday drivers will kill them. Let them take the subway to the end of the line and grab a cab from there."

"Right," said Bryan as he reached for the phone.

He was somewhat concerned about being able to raise the district men (non-writing reporters who are responsible for a fixed area), since they might well be out on a story.

But Suzy, the *Ledger's* favorite telephone operator, took over. "I'll get them," she said. "Don't you worry. I know every place they hang out. I'll have them in five minutes."

Reassured, Bryan sat back to await further instructions.

Holloway, in the meantime, was addressing the two lone reporters who had been summoned to his desk.

"Get out to Jackson Airport as fast as you can. You'll find plenty to do. Just don't fall over each other. Get as much detail as you can, eyewitness accounts, if possible. And be sure to get a passenger list."

Dismissed, the two hurried into their coats and left.

David had been keeping a vigilant watch over the news ticker, which had stopped erupting. He had read the bulletin as it came through and tingled at the thought of a good story. It had been an unusually quiet day, with little local news. It must be bedlam out there, he thought. No additional data—not even a statement from the airline yet. Just a burning plane.

David glanced up, startled to find the editor eyeing him speculatively. As he returned to the ticker, a small thrill of apprehension shot through him.

Holloway's eyes roamed the city room with its many empty desks. Again he thought with exasperation, what an hour for something to happen!

His eyes fell on the clock. He had ninety minutes to the next edition—but could delay it if need be. And he needed what he didn't have—man power. He knew he could not spare any of the four men on rewrite. They would have their hands full as soon as the facts started to pour in.

Frank Brownlow would write the lead story. Brownie was an old hand at catastrophes and never got excited. He worked best under pressure. Brownie would milk the leg men for whatever they picked up and turn out not only a terse, factual story, but also the most colorful one in town. No worry about Brownie.

A second rewrite man would do a side story—interviews with eyewitnesses. A third would get up sketches of the more prominent of the deceased. The fourth would put the passenger list together and check other angles. But these four men would have to be fed by the reporters heading for the scene of the crash.

The east side and west side district reporters were on their way, as were the two shipped out from the office. But this was nowhere near enough at a disaster story.

Suddenly Holloway came to a decision.

"David!" he called.

The copy boy sped to his side.

Holloway rummaged through a drawer, found what he was looking for and handed it to David.

"Here's a press card. It will get you through the police lines. Do you know how to get out to Jackson Airport? Good! Take some copy paper and pencils. Get what you can—and call in as soon as possible. Good luck."

Unexpectedly, his gray eyes softened and he extended his hand. "This will be a little different from anything you covered in college," he said quietly. "Just keep your wits about you and don't rattle." There was a brief handshake, after which Holloway turned and barked a command to his assistant, Bryan.

David hurried into his coat and out into the chill, wet night.

☆☆☆ *2*

EN ROUTE

IT WAS AS HE TOOK a seat in the half-empty subway car that David reflected that it hadn't taken so long, after all. Just nine months since he became a copy boy and now here he was—press card and all.

He took the card out and examined it minutely. Elation surged through him. This small cardboard shield, issued by the Police Department—such a little thing to mean so much. He had to fight down an impulse to shout, "Look, everybody—I've got a police card! I'm sitting next to you, and I look just like anybody—but really, I'm a reporter now!"

The thought was suddenly sobering. "Only temporarily," he added wryly to himself. "By tomorrow I may be the sad sack of the city room. They're too nice to say anything to me, but among themselves they'd say, 'Did you hear that Holly sent young White—the kid who runs copy—out on the plane crash? Poor kid didn't know much whether he was coming or going. Anyway, he had a nice, long subway ride.' "

David forced the humiliating thought from his mind and looked out the subway car window. The stations, at any rate, were familiar. Thank goodness, he thought, I know my way about town.

For David had applied himself assiduously to the transportation challenge of the big city. His second day in New York, he took the wrong subway train and was an hour late for his appointment with Mr. Holloway. When he explained his tardiness, the city editor's cool gray eyes flickered faintly with amusement.

"If it is your intention to become a reporter here," he said mildly, "you should realize that a news story is not going to wait while you change trains."

David discovered that the New York City telephone directories were a fount of information. Every subway line was mapped in detail, and he all but memorized them. He had visited—via subway—all the major points of interest and had been a frequent sight-seer at Jackson Airport, for which he was deeply thankful at the moment.

"Isn't it funny," David mused, "how you can work and work for something, and nothing will happen, and then, by purest accident, wham! there it is?"

For once, however, David was underestimating Holloway, for that gentleman rarely did anything without good reason. There were four other copy boys on duty that night, most of whom had been on the paper for a considerably longer time than David. To all cursory appearances, they seemed equally qualified for "the break." But Holloway, despite his detached appearance and frequently sarcastic manner, was fully aware of the potentials of all his employees. He had kept a particularly vigilant eye on David, ever since the time, no more than a month after he started work on the *Ledger,* when the copy boy had pinpointed a particular street in Greenwich Village. The two wire services had come in with conflicting addresses on the location of a street brawl. It was a minor story, which didn't even get into the paper—but a discussion started up as to which of the wire services was accurate.

David, who was bringing coffee up for the reporters, overheard the hassle and said, "I think both wire services could be right. It sounds crazy but, at one point, West Fourth Street and West Tenth Street intersect. So if one wire service says 'near the corner of W. Fourth,' and the other 'near the corner of W. Tenth'—they're only a few feet apart." Whereupon another reporter, who lived in the area, joined the conversation and corroborated David's statement.

Holloway, engrossed in checking copy at least ten feet distant, missed not a word of this. He raised his head and glanced briefly at David. Here was a young man who got lost in the subway barely a month ago and was already so familiar with the more esoteric areas of the city he could direct the natives. This would bear watching. And watch he did.

He noticed that as a copy boy, David didn't "ride the bench"—that is, stay seated until he heard somebody call "Copy!" Instead, he stationed himself close to the city desk, where he could see the typed sheets thrown into various in-

coming and outgoing baskets and channel them to their destinations. He read the newspaper thoroughly each day, but not while he was running copy, a habit common to copy boys which infuriated Holloway.

Most important to the city editor was the good will with which David performed the routine tasks assigned him. Within a week of running coffee and sandwiches, David knew without being told who drank "black with no sugar" to "light with three heaping spoons." Moreover, it was still hot when he delivered it. And on his trips to the "morgue" (library) to get the clippings so necessary for background information in writing a story, he did not dawdle and he made sure he brought back exactly what was asked for.

And so when Holly tapped David for the plane crash, he had infinitely more confidence in his decision than did the subject himself.

Arriving at the end of the subway line, David turned his coat collar up and walked out into a mist of cold and drizzle. The snow had become a mess of icy slush underfoot and there was not a taxi in sight. A fairly large group of people waiting desolately at the bus stop gave mute evidence of the fact that, if the buses were running at all, they were few and very far between.

The tyro reporter stood bewildered and irresolute in the street. This was something he hadn't anticipated—not even to be able to get there! Almost without thinking, he ran out into the road, toward the oncoming traffic, and waved down the first car that came along.

Holding his press card toward the driver, David pleaded, "Please, I'm with the *Ledger*. I've got to get to the airport quickly—there's been a bad crash."

The driver looked at the card and eyed David sharply. "That's a dangerous stunt to pull in weather like this. You're lucky my brakes held," he said sternly.

"You're right," David replied contritely. "But I have to get there."

"O.K. I'm going that way. Hop in."

Gratefully, David did so. As the warmth from the car heater hit his legs, he became aware that his feet were icy and wet. The deep slush had penetrated over the tops of his shoes and had now melted into icy puddles along the inside soles. He reflected that it probably would be a lot worse before the night was over.

"I heard the bulletin on the radio," said the driver. "It's a real mean night for a crash."

The headlights glowed fuzzily in the wet gloom of the night as the car moved cautiously through the slush.

Before long, David saw powerful searchlights slashing the dark sky. "Your wreck's out there somewhere," said the driver. "I'll drop you off at the Administration Building, O.K.?"

"Oh, just anywhere is fine. Say, I'm awfully grateful to you."

"That's all right," said the driver as the car stopped. "I'll look for your story in the *Ledger* tomorrow. So long."

David wanted to explain that it wouldn't be "his story"— that he didn't even know if he would contribute a single phrase to it—but common sense overrode modesty. He came to the conclusion he was to reach many times in the future— that the layman has vague and somewhat romantic notions of how a newspaper is put out, and does not want to be divested of them. The simplest way to handle the situation is to be noncommittal.

"That's fine," replied David cheerfully. "And thanks a million."

With a wave of the hand, the driver turned the window up and the car continued onward. David hurried toward the large building nearby lettered "Administration."

HOLOCAUST AT JACKSON AIRPORT

INSIDE THE ADMINISTRATION BUILDING all was chaos. A babble of voices rose and fell. One man was attempting to disengage himself from a circle of importuning people and David recognized the two *Ledger* reporters among them.

"We are making a full investigation. When we have the facts, we will make a statement. We cannot make a statement until we have all the facts. Please excuse me now." His voice was imploring. He was evidently an airline official, for he made a successful dash and found refuge in one of the private offices.

A policeman approached David. "You'll have to leave, buddy. Can't hang around here now!"

"I'm a reporter with the *Ledger*," said David, proffering his police card. The policeman examined it closely and then returned it. "You're gonna get yourself a case of bursitis if you keep that in your pocket all night," he said.

It was then David noticed that other reporters had either pinned their cards to their lapels or stuck them in their hatbands. He thereupon tucked his own card firmly into his hatband—where it could be seen by all. This also left his hands free to take notes. He felt a little sheepish as he realized that this act, which he had previously interpreted as that of a show-off or blow-hard, was merely a measure of expedience.

As he scanned the immediate area, he came to the conclusion that no exclusive data was going to emanate from here.

Besides, the two *Ledger* reporters had the situation well in hand—Ed Wales was planted in front of the door where the airline executive had disappeared, and Bill Evans was deep in conversation with World Wide Airline's publicity man.

David decided to see the wreck for himself. Since all planes were grounded after the crash, because of the weather, he walked out on the field.

Off in the distance, powerful searchlights were beating down on the scene of the conflagration, which appeared to be a good mile from the Administration Building. The field was alive with noisy activity. Ambulances were careening up and down the area. Police cars, with their sirens going full blast, were trying to open a path for the ambulances.

David knew instinctively that there would be no ride-hitching here, so he thrust his hands deep in his pockets, turned his collar up and started walking.

Afterwards, David recalled that he had never felt so useless and alone as he did picking his way across the icy, wet ground, in the general direction of the wreck. It was still burning fiercely. After walking a distance which seemed to have virtually no end, David finally approached a scene which indelibly impressed itself on his mind. It was right out of Dante's *Inferno*. Even at a distance of almost 1,000 feet, the heat was incredible. Firemen were fighting the sheets of flames with a foam substance. They looked like weird ghosts, their black rubber and asbestos uniforms speckled with white blotches. Restrained by the intense heat and the appalling scene, David could only stand and stare dumbly. Then the wind changed and the smell was overwhelming.

In the eerie white light of the blinding searchlights, he suddenly became aware that there were bodies lying all around. He stood paralyzed in his tracks. The physical and mental images shocked him almost into a state of stupor.

An angry, incredulous voice snapped him out of it. "What

are you doing here?" it demanded harshly. A police captain
loomed in front of him.

"You're not allowed here! No reporters, no nobody! We've
got a job to do!" His voice grew curious. "How'd you get over
here, anyway? We got lines up."

"I don't know," replied David honestly. He was surprised
at the sound of his voice, which miraculously gave no hint
of the turmoil and physical illness inside. "I walked here in
the dark, and I guess I must have walked around the lines."

"Well, you better walk back the same way or you'll get run
over. We've got a job to do fast, and nobody's expecting jay-
walkers!"

David nodded and began walking again. It was as though
a black cloud hovered about him. The wind shifted very
slightly and he sniffed gratefully at the wet, fresh air. Dully,
he thought, "I will never read a fire story again as long as I
live without remembering that smell." He looked at his watch.
It was *12:45*. "Good grief," he thought in amazement, "it's
less than two hours since I sat peacefully in the city room!"
He felt he had lived a whole lifetime—and actually, less than
two hours had elapsed.

The first time he heard the sound, he looked down at his
feet. They were making a noise, all right. His trousers were
virtually pasted to his legs from the calf down and his shoes
were a sodden mass of ice and white streaks—the fireman's
foam, he recalled. But even as he halted, he thought he heard
the sound again. Now he stood quite still, scarcely breathing,
and listened intently.

"Help! Please, help!" It was weak and low, but it was un-
mistakable.

"Keep talking—where are you?" David shouted.

"Here. I'm here. I'm hurt."

David veered over to the left. His eyes, which had become
accustomed to the dark, quickly spotted a mass huddled on

the ground.

"Thank God!" said the man. "I must have blacked out. My legs hurt. How long have I been here?"

There was something oddly familiar about that voice. David struck a match, cupped it in his hands and gasped as he recognized the handsome features of Scott Avery, an outstanding actor of the New York stage.

"You're all right, Mr. Avery. Just lie quietly and I'll get an ambulance. Don't try to move."

"I couldn't if I wanted to," replied the actor wryly. Then a note of fear entered his voice. "Look—do you have to go? I mean, will you be able to find me again? It's awfully dark and it's a big field."

David handed the actor his packet of matches. "Light them when you hear me calling you," he instructed. "And don't worry—I'll find you."

He started running toward the distant scene of activity, conserving his voice until there was a possibility that he might be heard. By great good fortune, he spotted an ambulance crossing the field, its distinctive red beacon going counter clockwise on the top. Shouting as he ran, he finally made himself heard and the driver swung the car lights in his direction.

"I've found an injured passenger. Is there a doctor aboard?"

In reply, the driver shifted into gear and guided his vehicle through the night toward the running figure. "Just injured?" he called out in amazement. "All we've been picking up is dead ones."

David climbed aboard and pointed in the general direction from which he had come, saying, "I'll tell you when to stop."

After a while, at David's direction, they stopped and, in response to his calls, a small flare of light was seen. With a doctor and two hospital attendants, David helped carry the injured actor into the ambulance.

On the ride to General Hospital, David had time to reflect

on the amazing turn of events. Obviously, not everyone aboard had been killed. Scott Avery was one of the few survivors, if not the lone survivor. Once at the hospital, David knew he wouldn't be allowed anywhere near the injured man. The time was now. He waited until the ambulance had left the airport and then took pencil and paper from his pockets. His fingers seemed frozen stiff.

Ordinarily, reporters are not allowed to ride ambulances. This David knew, and had taken the precautionary measure of tucking the press card in his pocket. The ambulance crew assumed he was a close friend or relative. They, too, had recognized the actor immediately. While Avery appeared to be in a bad way physically—his legs were evidently fractured and the internal injuries could not be assessed until he arrived at the hospital—he was mentally alert and not at all reluctant to talk.

"Mr. Avery," David began, "I saw you in two Broadway shows and I can't tell you how sorry I am to see you under these circumstances now. I'm David White and I'm with the *Ledger*. Could you answer some questions?"

The actor grinned.

"David, I've seen many people in my day—but I can tell you that I was never happier to see anyone in my life than I was to see you a while ago. Fire away."

"Tell me what happened."

And so, while David took notes as best he could in the speeding, jouncing ambulance, Scott Avery told his story.

"I have a contract with Colossal Films and was to report on the set Tuesday morning. Oh, well . . . I was one of the last persons to board the plane. This was a first class flight, with all seats reserved. Mine was on the port side, against an emergency exit door. We were supposed to take off at 9:02.

"About a minute or so before 9:00, a member of the plane crew told us there would be a slight delay. He indicated—

without quite saying so—that one of the motors had been acting up, that it was a minor malfunction and that we would be
delayed so short a time that we would make it up in flight.

"So I leaned back in my seat and went to sleep. I woke up
to the noise of the motors roaring. It was 10:10, and we
hadn't even taken off yet. They kept warming those motors
for almost twenty minutes, and then suddenly they stopped.
The loudspeaker announced that we would be taking off in a
few minutes. Finally, at 10:50, we began rolling down the
runway. I lay back to resume my snooze.

"We must have gone about a mile when the plane began
to rise off the ground. All of a sudden, there was a bad lurch.
I saw huge orange flames shooting out of the motor on the
extreme left, and then they spread to the motor right next to
it. I began to unfasten my safety belt.

"Then the plane banked sharply to the left, as if somebody
had lifted it from the other side and was trying to turn it up-
side down. I don't know much what happened after that—I
remember everybody screaming. I must have been thrown
clear of the plane and knocked unconscious. When I came to,
I was cold and wet and my legs hurt like the devil. I called for
a while and then you found me. . . . And now I'll never
read the *Transcript* again!" he wound up jocularly.

This was a reference to the *Ledger's* opposition.

"Oh, that's all right, Mr. Avery—by all means read the
Transcript," quipped David. "How else will you know how
much better the *Ledger* is?"

The actor laughed and then winced as the ambulance
pulled up to a stop in front of General Hospital.

David bounded out. "Good luck, Mr. Avery. I'll come and
see your next show."

"I'll send you a pass!"

There was a pay telephone booth in the lobby of the hospital and David made a beeline for it. His hands shaking

slightly, he dialed the *Ledger* and shouted, "Suzy, quick give me the city desk."

"I got an interview with a survivor—Scott Avery," David said excitedly to Bryan, the assistant night city editor, who picked up the phone.

"Hold it, Dave," Bryan urged. "I'll put Burton on. Tell him the facts and don't leave anything out. Looks like Avery is the only survivor. Oh, wait a minute—Mr. Holloway wants to talk to you for a minute before Burton takes you on rewrite."

"David?" Mr. Holloway's voice questioned. "Do I understand you have an interview with Scott Avery?"

"Yes, sir."

"Fine. Do all the papers have it?"

"No, sir. I have it alone. You see, I happened . . ."

Holloway cut in, "You have it alone? Then let's not waste time. I'll put Burton on—tell him exactly what happened and exactly what Avery told you. That's a page one story, all by itself. Hold on. . . . Burton! Pick up David White on Number 2."

☆☆☆ *4*

THE NEXT DAY

DAVID HARDLY SLEPT that night. He got back to his room at the Y in midtown after three o'clock. It was a pleasant enough room, but now he found it very confining. He kept pacing it, after turning on the radio and switching to an all-night station featuring popular recorded music and news. Within a short time, the announcer cut in with a bulletin:

"Police now report that there was one survivor—actor Scott Avery—on the ill-fated Superliner which crashed on take-off from Jackson Airport. We repeat—Scott Avery is alive. His injuries have not yet been determined. Stay tuned for further details."

That meant only one thing—that the *Ledger* had a clean two-hour beat on the Avery story and had it all wrapped up in its second edition, the one that got the greatest circulation. Not only did the *Ledger* have Avery identified, but it also had his own story—the kind of stuff in which newspaper readers are vitally interested.

It was daybreak before David fell off into a fitful sleep, which was marred by bizarre nightmares.

About eight o'clock, he dressed and went out to the corner newsstand to pick up a copy of the *Ledger*. There, on the top of page 1, was the headline, "SCOTT AVERY'S OWN STORY," with a subheading, *"Found by Reporter, Actor's Survival Miraculous."*

Oblivious of his surroundings, David stood there and read the story through slowly, as though completely ignorant of its content. Then he headed for a nearby cafeteria and ate a huge breakfast.

On his way back to the Y, David also picked up a copy of the *Transcript* and spent the next hour reading both papers thoroughly, sprawled in the one comfortable chair in his room. He noted with satisfaction that the *Transcript* had little more than the bare police report of Avery's survival. No visitors were permitted to see the actor, and David could well imagine the consternation in the city room of the *Transcript* when the second edition of the *Ledger* arrived there!

David sat back to reflect on how much good luck plays a

part in being successful. Quite a bit, he decided.

In that respect, David did himself an injustice. He was lucky only in that he knew what he wanted to do. He had known since his freshman year at State College that he wanted to do newspaper work—and he had set about learning it from the bottom up.

Before David was born, his father, a chemist, had lived in New York City for a number of years and even after he had moved to Indiana, he continued to read the New York *Ledger,* to which he subscribed by mail. The *Ledger,* so distinctively well written, with its sports columnists, Washington writers and feature stories, was as familiar to David all through his childhood as his mother's cookie jar.

He had always loved writing, too. It didn't come easily to him—but that was because he was a perfectionist and carefully searched his mind for the precise word. Certainly, he didn't groan with dismay, as many of his friends did, when there was a book report or an English composition for homework. He preferred them any day to, say, mathematics.

His first year at college, David applied for a place on the school newspaper. As a freshman, he carried proofs to the printer, helped solicit ads, did whatever he was told. After a while, he was permitted to cover the college tennis meets, the faculty meetings, etc. In his final year, he was editor of the college newspaper.

When he mentioned to his father that he was happiest at the college paper and wanted to make reporting his life's work, his dad had told him, "Write to the *Ledger.* If you're going to work on a newspaper, you might just as well try to work on the best one."

And so, a few months before graduation, David had sent a letter off to E. E. Holloway, city editor of the New York *Ledger.*

Holloway's reply was polite but noncommital:

Through the years we have had numerous instances where copy boys have advanced to reporters. While I certainly would not guarantee anything, some of our best staff members did start that way. How you fare at the *Ledger* is entirely up to you. I will certainly make no promises.

This was more than enough for David. Fresh from college as he was, he was honest enough to realize that all he could offer a big city newspaper was a willingness to learn.

He had learned a great deal in the past nine months of running copy.

He had learned, for instance, that a newspaper is as distinctive as a person. Every paper had a style book, dealing in good part with abbreviations and spellings.

David frequently wondered why such importance was attached to the fact, for instance, that on the *Ledger* the title "junior" at the end of a man's name had to appear "jr.," with a small "j." Yet he supposed habit was as strongly ingrained in a newspaper as it was in people, so the best thing was to go along with it. Every paper had similar idiosyncrasies. . . . The *Ledger* spelled "kidnaped" with one "p" while the *Transcript* spelled it with two "p's." He checked the dictionary. Both spellings were correct.

He knew that all copy on the *Ledger* had to be triple-spaced. That made it easy for the city desk or the man on the copy desk, where copy was further checked and the headlines were written, to insert changes where necessary. This still left the copy legible enough for the printer in the composing room.

It was the "slugs" that fascinated David most. Every story had a slug for identification purposes. A slug, he noted, was always one word, and descriptive. A murder story, for instance, would be slugged "slay," a robbery "rob," a police shake-up "cop," a shooting "shoot."

Many a time, as an involved story got under way, David would think, "Let's see the slug they put on that one!" But the desk never faltered. They always came up with a slug, and it was always apt—and sometimes very ingenious.

Once there were three unrelated murders. He wondered how that would be handled. One was slugged "slay," a second "murder" and the third "homicide." Simple!

As he sat there musing in his room at the Y, the events of the past twenty-four hours seemed suddenly to catch up with him. He wasn't due at the *Ledger* until 4 p.m. He loosened his tie, lay down on the bed and almost immediately fell into a deep sleep.

When David walked into the *Ledger's* city room that afternoon, he was more than a little self-conscious.

Holloway greeted him with a firm handshake and a booming, "Fine job, kid." Several reporters came over to him, including two of the "greats," and congratulated him. They asked him to relate exactly what had happened, and before David knew it, almost half of the city room seemed to be standing in a circle around him, listening to his account.

Somewhat embarrassed, he stole a glance at Holloway, who appeared busy at his desk. But from the alert tilt of his head, David sensed he was listening, too. Everybody burst into laughter a few minutes later when there was a call of "Copy!" and David hastily said, "Excuse me"—and went to answer the call.

He was soon back into the groove of running copy, going to the composing room for proofs of stories for other reporters —and running coffee. Fame, he reflected, was as transitory in the newspaper business as elsewhere.

★★★ 5

DAVID BECOMES A LEG MAN

ONE DAY, a week later, when the continuing investigation into the airplane crash had been reduced to two paragraphs in the back pages of the *Ledger*, Holloway beckoned
to David.

"Son," Holly said, "how would you like to be a district
man?"

Before David could answer, Holloway went on:

"Steve Martin has been covering the east side for us for
the last two years, and I think he's about ready to come inside
and do general reporting. He should do all right. That leaves
an opening here. Think you'd like it?"

David strove to keep the eagerness out of his voice.

"I'm sure of it, Mr. Holloway. And thanks."

It was two minutes before 6 p.m. when David walked down
a block typical of many on the east side of Manhattan. Expensive, modern, elevator apartment buildings were side by
side with old tenements and brownstone houses. Various
stores occupied the street level. David pushed open the door
of one particularly nondescript store—and entered the east
side shack.

It was really a small, glass-fronted store which had been
converted into an office. A faded green curtain covered the
plate glass window, and from the outside the place looked
as if it might be a hangout for gamblers. In fact, on numerous
occasions, strangers had furtively opened the front door,

21

poked their heads in and whispered conspiratorially, "Can a guy place a bet on a horse here?"

The usual answer to that was, "Only on horses that run in Mexico."

The disappointed visitor would realize he was being ribbed and would ask plaintively, "Just what is this place, anyway? I've been walking past here for years, and I've never quite been able to figure it."

When David stepped inside, he took in the rather shabby furnishings—four ancient desks and straight-backed chairs, a small sink. The dull tan walls were covered with a motley assortment of pictures of movie stars, politicians, criminals, sports figures. In the one incongruous easy chair lounged the room's sole occupant—Bill Baxter, of the American Press, a wire service which fed all New York City newspapers. Baxter was forty-five years old and he had been with the Press for twenty years, the last ten covering the east side for his news service. Because of a huge shock of snow-white hair, he looked older than his years. He was a relaxed, easygoing man who knew the city and knew his job—and gave unstintingly of his knowledge.

"I'm David White, of the *Ledger*," David said.

Baxter touched the rim of his glasses and looked up. He saw a sandy-haired youth, with intelligent brown eyes and sharply defined features, his ready smile softening the narrow contours of his face. Because of his lean physique, David looked taller than his actual height of five feet ten inches. His hair was a modified crew cut.

"Hello," Baxter said, easing his way out of the comfortable chair. "Welcome to our humble abode! I heard you were coming to replace Steve Martin. This is my chair—I brought it here when my wife threw it out of the house. . . . Say, aren't you the guy responsible for that Scott Avery interview? That was quite a job."

"Thank you very much, Mr. Baxter," David said, relaxing considerably.

"Cut that 'Mr. Baxter' business. My name is Bill—that's what all my friends call me. Behind my back, I'm also known as 'Pappy'—but it doesn't bother me. The hair may be gray—but it's all there. That's more than a lot of guys can say. Your desk is this one over here. It has a telephone connected directly to the *Ledger* office."

"Whose desks are these others?"

"This one in the center is mine—American Press. Those other two belong to Andy Stewart, of the *Transcript,* and Dick Whelan, of the *Chronicle.*"

"Kind of a small office for four people," David noted.

"Sure is," Baxter agreed. "But it's comfortable in the wintertime and in the summer we often sit outside, watching the pretty girls go by. . . . I think you'll like it—the job, that is. The girls, too—come to think of it!"

David eyed Baxter hesitantly for a moment, then apparently made up his mind.

"Can I ask you something, Bill?"

"Certainly," replied Baxter, "that's what I'm here for—first-aid center to new reporters!"

"That's for me, first aid!" returned David feelingly. "Look, just what is my job? I mean, what am I supposed to do? Nobody told me!"

There was a hint of panic in David's voice, despite its bantering tone, and Baxter was touched by the young man's candor. Lots of new reporters had come and gone down here, and many of them—too many of them—were brash and knowing. This was refreshing honesty and Baxter warmed to it.

"You're responsible for the whole east side," he replied.

"What does that mean?"

"The east side is an area of several square miles with fixed boundaries. You are responsible for every crime, accident, fire and tragedy in that area. It's not quite as imposing as it sounds."

"How do I learn about what's going on?"

"In one of three ways. First, there's a police station right across the street from here. You'll be spending a lot of time in there, and you may be there on numerous occasions when some kind of emergency call comes in.

"Second—and this will be your most frequent source of action—your city desk will call you, give you the outline on a story and send you moving on it. It is no reflection on you that the city desk, on the other side of town, is familiar with a story which is breaking perhaps no more than a block from the shack; they know of it because of a very intricate communication system practiced by the Police Department. Whenever there is any kind of police action—any incident on which police roll, the precinct handling it must send a quick, brief report to the Communications Bureau, at Police Headquarters. Now, all the newspapers—and wire services, too—have district men at Police Headquarters. As soon as these reporters see a flash which looks promising, they call their city desks, which, in turn, call the district men covering that particular area. You are responsible not only for the precinct across the street but for three other precincts in this area. Obviously, you can't be in four places at one time. Say there has been an explosion in the East Nineties. The precinct which has jurisdiction will flash headquarters, giving the address and what few details it has. The *Ledger* reporter at Police Headquarters will either call you directly or call the city desk, which will pass the information along to you. Then you'll roll on it—and get the whole story. It's the only way you can cover a city of this size."

David nodded thoughtfully; it seemed an excellent system and one calculated to get the complete story and get it fast.

Then he remembered something and asked, "But you said there were three ways of learning about news, and you've only mentioned two. What's the third?"

Baxter laughed. "The third is the blessing and the bane of all city desks—tipsters. Some are constant readers and some are constant headaches—but you have to at least go through the motions with a tip; it might be a real news beat."

"You mean the people who call up with information?" David queried.

"That's them," replied Baxter. "Sometimes it can be of real value—if the tip is accurate—in getting photographers to the scene fast. But very often we have to chase down a phoney story, invented by a tipsy practical joker.

"All kinds of people call newspaper city desks," he continued. "I know, I used to work on one. I think maybe that's one reason why I asked to go back on a district. I don't like to be hemmed in by telephones. And besides, I like action— even if I never get to write anything. Maybe when my legs start giving out, I'll ask to go back on the city desk. Right now, I'm content to stay on as a leg man. I like to move around."

David was somewhat relieved to hear that Bill Baxter was a district man through choice. It hadn't seemed fair that a man of his obvious ability should be so restricted. Apparently, it was a matter of opinion—Baxter felt confined in the city room and relaxed in the district, where, in a sense, he was his own boss.

"A lot of things you'll learn as you go along," Baxter continued. "But I'll fill you in on certain fundamentals. Don't worry. It's impossible to blueprint this entire job."

"Whew!" David sighed with relief. "I sure appreciate what you've told me. All information gratefully received and acknowledged!"

"Your hours are the same as mine—6 p.m. to 2 a.m.," Bax-

ter continued, smiling. "I guess you've been told by your city
desk what days you'll be off."

"Tuesday and Wednesday," replied David with a grimace.

"Those, whether you realize it or not, are excellent days off.
At first, most people think they'd like Saturday and Sunday
off. Where can you go summers during week ends in the city?
Every place is jammed and the prices are double. You go to
the same place on a Tuesday or Wednesday, you have more
conveniences—such as the beaches—you pay less money,
and you have the place to yourself. Certainly it's easier to
get theater tickets for a weekday night."

"Who works for me on my nights off?" David asked.

"Charley Simmons. He's the *Ledger's* swing man. Swing
man means that he swings from one district to another, to
cover the regular men's days off. I know he works the west
side two nights a week for the *Ledger's* man over there, Harry
Thornton. You'll probably never bump into them because of
different nights off."

"What divides the east side from the west side?" David
asked.

"Fifth Avenue. I should have told you that without your
asking. I've been in this job so long that I take certain things
for granted. Specifically, you take everything east from the
east side of Fifth Avenue. The west side man takes everything
west from the west side of Fifth Avenue. However, one thing
ought to be made abundantly plain to you. If your office asks
you to cover something which is not in your district—something west of Fifth Avenue—don't say, 'That's out of my district.' Your city desk knows the boundaries quite well and the
west side man may be tied up."

David nodded, then said, "Something I've always been curious about—when a shooting or a stick-up or an accident
happens in the middle of the street, a street that is the boundary of two precincts, how do the police work it out? I mean,

who gets the credit for the arrest, if it's an arrest, that is?"

Baxter chortled. "Who wants credit? You'll have to go over to the precinct with me and see for yourself the amount of paper work required for any police action. I think most of them would gladly pass up the glory, along with the paper work.

"There's a famous old story about Fifth Avenue and 42nd Street, which used to be the boundary of four different precincts—two on the east side and two on the west side. One day, in the exact center of the intersection, a car broke down. You know what happened? A cop from each precinct took a whack at pushing the car into his neighbor's domain—so he wouldn't get stuck with the paper work!"

David chuckled and asked with relish, "What finally happened?"

"I don't know," Baxter chuckled, too. "I don't even know if the story is true. . . . It's one of those things somebody told me years ago. But it could be!

"Then there's the one where a cop could not spell Kosciusko Street. So he shoved a stolen car he had just recovered around the corner to Smith Street."

David laughed and Baxter continued, "There are a million stories—some not exactly funny. But don't get the idea that cops are dumb. Not these days. There's a new breed coming in. Let's go across the street to the precinct and meet some of the boys."

The sun had set and the two green lamps in front of the precinct were shining. They gave off an eerie glow. There was a flagpole jutting out of the second floor of the brownstone building, which had a stoop with five steps leading to it.

As the two newspapermen walked into the building proper, the floor creaked. It was an old building, standing at least eighty years. The ceiling was extremely high. To the right, behind a huge raised desk, sat a police officer, a lieutenant.

Just before the desk was a wooden railing—with the neatly
lettered sign on it:

NOBODY GOES BEYOND THIS RAILING WITHOUT PERMISSION.
BY ORDER OF CAPT. JOHN J. MORRISON.

"Lieutenant McCarthy, this is David White, the new district man for the *Ledger,*" Baxter said in introduction.

"What happened to Steve Martin?" the officer asked, then
added jokingly, "This district work too much for him?"

"He's working out of the office now," replied David.

"Lieutenant," Baxter said, "can we take a look at an aided
card? I'd like to show David just what that is—since he'll be
seeing plenty of them, and he might as well learn how to read
them."

The lieutenant handed over a reddish pink card, about five
by eight inches.

"Every time police respond to any call involving physical
injury—a fight, a fire, night club brawl, accident or what
have you," Baxter explained, "an aided card must be made
out. Here, this card I'm holding deals with an auto accident.
As you see, it lists the victim's name, his age, his address, his
injuries. It shows which hospital he was taken to. It also lists
the name of the operator of the car which hit him—as well as
the license plate number on that car. It mentions that the car
was going north on First Avenue, forty feet south of 52nd
Street when the man was hit.

"The policeman who phoned in this report to the clerical
man—another police officer—did not see the accident, of
course. Had he seen it, he would have so stated on the aided
card. It's extremely rare that a policeman is a witness to such
an accident.

"Now the card does not say who was at fault in this accident. It would appear that the victim—being hit forty feet
south of the corner—did not start to cross at the intersection.

However, unless the cops actually tell you that the man crossed in the middle of the street, you cannot say so on your own. Stick to exactly what is on the aided card. You'll avoid trouble that way. Incidentally, not anybody can come in here and look at these cards."

"Aren't they public records?" David asked.

"Yes and no," Baxter answered. "What if a lawyer for that accident victim came in here and looked at the card and, to help his client, scratched out the fact that the accident happened forty feet south of the intersection?"

"Isn't the man's lawyer entitled to know what is on the official police report—to establish possible negligence on the part of the driver?" David asked.

"Good question," Baxter answered. "He makes a formal request for the data at police headquarters and the information is mailed to him. In that way, there is no possible chance of shenanigans."

Lieutenant McCarthy, listening attentively to this basic instruction, cut in with: "Aren't you going to tell him about those ambulance-chasing lawyers and the scandal of a few years ago?"

"Oh, that's ancient history. Why bring that up?" asked Baxter.

"You mean you're not going to tell Davey here about that scandal?" the desk officer demanded, his shrewd blue eyes wide open in mock surprise. "I bet a doughnut you've already filled him in with a few of those old chestnut cop stories!"

Baxter had the grace to flush. *"Touché,* Loot. You win. Maybe it'll be just as well for David, as a beginner on the street, to know it at that."

"Know about what?" David asked.

"It was a beautiful racket—while it lasted," Baxter began. "There were a couple of district men—never mind who they were—who used to grab hold of aided cards the moment they were made out in a certain precinct. Say it was an auto accident, maybe similar to the one we just looked at. These two reporters—and so far as I know there were only two so involved in the whole city—would call up a ring of lawyers and give them the vital details—where, when, etc.

"Within minutes, a lawyer would be buttonholing a relative of the victim—wife, or something like that—and talk her into retaining him as counsel in the case. Often the wife wouldn't even be aware of what she was doing, the lawyer grabbing her when she was hysterical and getting her to sign a legal contract.

"Of course, the reporters involved weren't doing this for love, you understand. They got a nice cut from the lawyers. Somehow, word of the racket got to the city desks of the two reporters involved. They admitted their part in the scheme but insisted they were unaware that they had done anything wrong, legally. They were fired."

"And arrested," the lieutenant added. "And convicted."

"That's true," Baxter said. "Each got a suspended sentence. I don't know what they're doing now."

☆☆☆ 6

REWRITE MEN DON'T BITE

IN THE NEXT FEW WEEKS, David saw a pretty good cross section of big city life. It was his first spring in New York and a far cry from the town in which he grew up in Indiana.

He was beginning to feel cramped in his quarters at the Y. It irritated him to have to come to his room after work and tiptoe around, lest he wake the young men in the adjoining rooms. He wanted a small apartment of his own, where he could have more room, a small refrigerator, perhaps, for a snack—something more home-like. And he began to watch the classified columns of the papers for a small flat priced within his means.

In the meantime, he was applying himself to his trade.

It took David a while to learn just how to give in a story to a rewrite man.

As a district reporter, he did not write for the *Ledger*. His job was to get the facts—from the police, firemen, neighbors, onlookers, etc.—and phone them in. The rewrite man would take care of the rest.

Rewrite men, David had heard, were a strange breed who gobbled up new district reporters and made them rue the day they first hankered to be newspapermen.

This, he soon found, was something of an exaggeration. Most of them had gone through the same apprenticeship that David was experiencing right now. In their day "on the street" they had to phone in to rewrite men, too—and it was as district reporters, specializing in crime, that they learned so much about the city, and especially how police and firemen worked.

What the rewrite men demanded were hard facts, presented in an orderly fashion, with a summary at the outset. For instance, when David was calling in about a stick-up of a jewelry store, they didn't want him to begin his presentation with details—which is what he did at the beginning.

"Look," Roger Mulvaney, a veteran rewrite man on the *Ledger,* said on the phone one evening to David. "It'll be a lot easier for you and for me if you do it my way. Don't try to write the story for me, though I know there is an awful tendency to do so.

"Before you go into the details of any story, give me an outline. For instance, you might tell me, 'I have a story involving the robbery of a jewelry shop by two armed men who got away with loot valued at $40,000. Nobody was hurt and the men fled in a black sedan, driven by a third accomplice at the wheel.'

"Then, when I know the general pitch from that brief summary—and only then—do you go into details. You begin by telling me the place of the occurrence; the name of the store, if any; the time; the name of the victim and what his relationship to the store is. And just what the thugs and their victim did and said during the robbery."

This, David realized, was only good common sense.

But David's inexperience continued to show—and he also learned never to guess when he was dealing with hard news.

One evening he phoned in a brief story dealing with the hold-up of a liquor store. The proprietor, whom David questioned a few minutes after the crime, said that the lone gunman had jumped into a taxi which was parked in front of the store and sped away.

"The cab went west on 46th Street in making its getaway," David told the rewrite man, who happened to be Roger Mulvaney again.

"Went which way?" Mulvaney asked, incredulity in his tone.

"Er—west," David repeated.

"Did anybody tell you that? And if so—who was it?"

"Why nobody did—I just assumed that's the way it went," David replied, on the defensive.

"For your information, junior, 46th Street is an eastbound street. Always has been—unless they changed it tonight. And I doubt that. Did the liquor store owner say that the cab went west on an eastbound street?"

There was a momentary silence, and then a crushed David replied, "No, he didn't. I suppose if it had, he would have mentioned it to me."

Mulvaney caught the chastened voice, and his own normally sarcastic tone gentled.

"Of course, he would—and the cab would have gotten bottled up in traffic, too—and not made a getaway! Now remember this, and never forget it—NEVER GUESS."

"I'm sorry," David said humbly. "It won't ever happen again."

Mulvaney continued, "Here's an easy way to remember how streets run in Manhattan: 'East is even—otherwise odd.' Of course, there are a few exceptions—every rule has some exceptions—but for the most part: 'East is even—otherwise odd.'"

From then on, David realized that an eastbound street in all likelihood was an even-numbered one and a westbound street was most likely an odd-numbered one.

☆☆☆ 7

WHAT'S A GOOD STORY?

DAVID SUFFERED occasional rebuffs in the course of his "on-the-job training," as he called it. Fortunately, he was sensible enough to realize that nothing personal was involved, and he learned from his mistakes.

It was mostly his perspective that was off—a common happening with tyro reporters. It was very difficult to be in the midst of some highly emotional proceedings and be able to regard them in their proper context amid the day's big news events.

For instance, he was present at the precinct one evening when two business men came in, shouting and cursing at one another.

"What seems to be the trouble?" the lieutenant on the desk inquired.

"He borrowed $1,000 from me six months ago," the first man said. "The loan was for only three months. He hasn't repaid a single cent. I want to have him arrested."

"Did you borrow the money from him?" the lieutenant asked the second man, who stood with head bowed at the desk.

"Yes, I did, officer—but my business has been going bad. I hope to pay it all back shortly, though—with full interest."

"You see," the complainant shouted. "He admits it. He admits that he borrowed the money from me and he hasn't paid it back. I want him arrested."

"Sorry, but I can't oblige," the lieutenant told him. "This is not a police matter," he pointed out, "it's a civil matter. There is nothing I can do about this. You can (here the lieutenant pointed to the complainant) go into Small Claims Court, get a warrant and sue for your money. Maybe the court will let you attach part of this man's business."

David offered this story to his city desk, telling James Bryan what he had.

"Oh, no," Bryan said. "That sort of thing, you will find, happens in every precinct in the city every day in the week. If we were to print that type of story, we'd have no room for anything else. But thanks, anyway."

Similarly, David soon realized that his desk was not overly interested in a woman reporting to the police that her eight-year-old son's bicycle had been stolen from the carriage room of her apartment building.

"Have there been a whole series of thefts from this carriage room?" Bryan asked.

"No," David replied. "Police say that there was a similar theft of a bicycle, from another family, about six months ago."

"Well, we'll skip this one. Maybe if there had been a whole slew of thefts, or if this last stolen bicycle was taken under unusual circumstances, we might be interested for a couple of paragraphs. Wait a minute—was the kid the son of some city official or something like that?"

"No, his father is a mechanic in a garage. I have the name of the garage, too."

"Forget it."

David tried to make it a practice to write every story that he gave in. It was interesting—especially during the first few months that he was on the district—to compare how these stories finally appeared in the *Ledger,* written by the rewrite man to whom he gave the story, and how David composed them himself.

Consequently, this is what he wrote after phoning in a story about a child who was run over by a truck:

Francis Harper, six years old, son of Mr. and Mrs. John Harper, of 984 Kingston Street, was hit and killed instantly by a truck operated by Frank Newhouse, thirty-six, of 614 Northern Avenue, and employed by the Speedy Trucking Company, of 202 Franklin Street, at 6:15 p.m., last night, at the intersection of First Avenue and Main Street, when he ran into the street after a ball, disregarding the traffic light signal. The truck driver was not arrested.

This is the way the rewrite man handled those same facts for the *Ledger:*

A six-year old boy, running for a ball, was fatally injured by a truck at 6:15 o'clock last evening, at the intersection of First Ave. and Main St.

He was Francis Harper, son of Mr. and Mrs. John Harper, of 984 Kingston St. Police identified the driver as Frank Newhouse, thirty-six, of 614 Northern Ave., employed by the Speedy Trucking Co., of 202 Franklin St.

Mr. Newhouse told police that the child, who was pronounced dead on arrival of an ambulance surgeon, had ignored a red light. The driver was not held.

David began to realize that jamming everything into the first sentence was no way to write a news story. He became even more deeply aware, as he read his own paper and other newspapers—especially his own—of the dictatorial thing called style. No newspaper had exactly the same style.

For instance, the *Ledger* always wrote out a person's age—not 6 or 36, but six and thirty-six. It also abbreviated Street and Avenue, as it did Company. But it took him a longer while to appreciate what was wrong with "6:15 p.m. last night."

"6:15 p.m., could not be morning, could it?" a rewrite man said to him. "But don't worry about it. I used to do it so much around here that I got to be known as 'Mr. Redundant.' Holly used to send my copy back to me and he'd circle that sort of thing in deep red crayon and print boldly at the top: 'Nothing like making it absolutely plain for the reader, eh?' "

☆☆☆ *8*

THE "FULL MOONERS"

THERE WERE FOUR PRECINCTS in his district and David visited them several times a night, always keeping in touch with his city desk at the *Ledger* by telephone.

"One of the cardinal rules in this business," Baxter had told

David, "is to keep in touch with your office. You're like a cop or a fireman—when your office wants you, they generally want you in a hurry. I even make it a habit to let my desk know where I'm going to eat—and the restaurant's phone number."

The several square miles in the area David was responsible for had a population ranging from the extremely rich to the very poor, with a good sprinkling of middle-class citizens. They all got the same treatment from the police.

Thanks to the fact that he was an accredited newspaper man, David was allowed to stand at the rail of the lieutenant's desk as all sorts streamed into the station houses.

It was amazing the number of people who had—or claimed to have "connections at City Hall" or were "personal friends of the Police Commissioner." It did them no good at all with the desk officers.

"Officer, Officer, I'm being followed," an elderly woman complained to a lieutenant one evening.

"Who's following you, madam?" the officer asked patiently.

"That man—he's very tall and very thin. He's also dark. He wants to murder me."

"What man? Where is he?"

"He's around the corner. You don't think he'd follow me into the station house, do you?"

"Why is he following you and why does he want to harm you, madam?"

"He knows that I have a beautiful daughter and he wants me to force her to marry him. She doesn't want to marry him."

There was a wild look in the woman's eyes. On the ready, David figured he was going to be an eyewitness to the arrest of a murder suspect. He had visions of the lieutenant leaping from behind his desk and running out into the street to apprehend the man—or at least sending some other police officers out to do so, from the rear room of the precinct, known as the muster room.

Instead, the lieutenant stroked his chin and said to the woman:

"Madam, just before you came in here, the man who was following you suddenly realized that he was not in love with your daughter at all. I know because he telephoned me and told me so."

"Are you sure, Officer?"

"Positive—you have my word for it. Now you go home and have a nice sleep."

"Oh, thank you so much, Officer!" The woman's voice softened with relief, and the agitated look left her eyes. "I appreciate what you just told me."

As the woman walked out of the station house—seemingly at peace with the world—David turned perplexed eyes on the lieutenant. The whole colloquy was fantastic. The officer soon explained:

"David, that woman has been coming into this precinct every night in the week for six months—always with the same story. It never varies an iota. We go through the same routine all the time. The dialogue never changes one word—almost as if she and I had rehearsed the whole thing and we were on the stage. It always winds up the same way—I tell her to go home and have a nice sleep. She always obeys me.

"She is absolutely harmless. It's just that she has delusions. She is lonely. She has no daughter. She has no children at all. She never had any. She was married, but her husband died many years ago. We checked her case out when she first came in here—that's why I know what I'm talking about."

"And I thought I was about to have a good story for the *Ledger*," David said ruefully.

"David," declared the lieutenant thoughtfully, "no one would believe you if you were to write up the characters that wander in here regularly."

The lieutenant was right.

David met many strange characters—especially the "full mooners."

In the space of a few hours one evening, as David stood by, the lieutenant of one precinct had this to contend with:

A woman, a social registerite, was hailed into the station house by a taxi driver who said that she had directed him to drive around the city's largest park eighteen times.

"Remember," the woman had advised the taxi driver as the trip began, "I want you to stop every time you see a horse. I want to give each one of them a lump of sugar."

The taxi driver said that during the eighteen trips around the huge park they had seen ten horses—each pulling a hansom. He had dutifully stopped his cab a total of 180 times—the woman had kept count. . . . Finally, she announced:

"I have no more sugar. I also don't have any money."

The lieutenant was about to enter the woman's name in the police ledger or blotter—where no erasures are allowed—when she suddenly said, "I just wanted to see what would happen." Then she reached into her purse and paid off the taxi driver, also giving him a ten-dollar tip.

A man with a long, smoke-stained beard came in next. In a ringing voice, he declaimed, "I just got the news from a secret source I am not at liberty to disclose!"

"What news?" the resigned lieutenant asked.

"The world is coming to an end at 6:04 p.m. tomorrow, Greenwich mean time. That is four hours later than our time in this city, where it will be 2:04 p.m." He looked gleefully around the room. "No point in taking shelter," he declared. "It will do you no good!"

Then he strode out.

The next visitor was a young man of about twenty-eight. This was his lament:

"I'm a physicist. You are a police officer. You know all about police work. I know all about physics and the sciences.

It has long been the theory that the world is round. I have established that this is false. You think maybe I believe it is square? You think wrong. It has nineteen sides."

He finally left under his own steam, too.

After three more such strangers had come and gone, the lieutenant turned to David and said:

"You wouldn't believe it if you didn't see it, would you? But there they are, Davey—and mostly they're harmless."

He laughed at the disbelief in David's eyes.

"I know just what you're thinking—they almost drove me batty in the beginning, too. But now I'm a pretty good psychologist. Look, all they want really is someone to listen to them. We're sitting ducks. Only," he added with a sigh, "on busy nights they drive me nuts!"

"Does this go on throughout the city?" asked David.

"Pretty much," was the reply. "A big city seems to attract such characters. They come from all over. But we've had more than our quota tonight.

"Wait a minute—this must be the night of the full moon. Every time there is a full moon, they turn up from wherever and come into station houses. I don't know what the moon does to them. The moon, you know, has an effect on tides. But it also has an effect on people."

Then the lieutenant turned to the sergeant who was on the switchboard and said, "Higgins, hold the fort a minute. I'm going to take a look."

The lieutenant left his desk, brushed by David, loped down the steps of the precinct, stood on the sidewalk and glanced up to the sky. Then he came back in, a victorious grin on his face.

"I told you," he said. "That moon is full—plenty full. Oh, boy!" he groaned. "Is this gonna be a night?"

David went back to the shack. In it were Baxter, Andy Stewart of the *Transcript* and Dick Whelan of the *Chronicle*.

Baxter was reading a current best seller. Stewart, a short, heavy-set man of thirty-five, and Whelan, about forty, medium-sized and balding, were playing cards.

Stewart, working for the *Ledger's* principal competitor, had not been especially warm toward David. It was not that he disliked David; it was just that, for some reason he himself could not explain, he never took to "new" people. As for Whelan, he never spoke very much—even to old-timers. Entire nights would go by and Whelan would not utter more than a half a dozen words.

"Lieutenant McCarthy must think me awfully green," David said as he entered the shack.

Baxter took his eyes from his book. Stewart and Whelan continued to play cards.

"Why?" Baxter asked.

"Oh, he's just been pulling my leg and thinks I don't realize it," David said.

"He is a practical joker, I know," Baxter said. "What's he up to?"

"Well, some strange characters walked into the precinct just now—one after the other. When the last one left, the lieutenant went out into the street, looked up at the sky, saw a full moon—and said that was the cause of these people dropping into the precinct. He called them 'full mooners.' "

"So?" Baxter said as the two other reporters momentarily interrupted their card game to exchange a knowing smile.

"So!" replied David flatly. "How stupid does he think I am? Full moon! The full moon had as much to do with those people in the station house as the price of tea in China!"

"I've got news for you, Dave," replied Baxter. "McCarthy is right as rain."

The look of pure disbelief in the young reporter's face caused Baxter to become a little truculent. "I'll tell you what," he continued, "I'm not a betting man—but I'll give you eight-to-five that the official police records bear me out. You go check the dates of the full moons, then check the police blotters. You'll find the 'full mooners' are a hard fact and no fiction!"

When the next Tuesday rolled around, David decided to put his day off to a special use. After checking statistics for three years back at Police Headquarters, he made a tour of the other three precincts in his territory and then dropped by at two other busy precincts in Manhattan. The raw material was so fascinating, he decided to write a story. He took copious notes on the "full mooners" at all sources.

Back at the Y, David started to frame his article. The "lead"—opening paragraph—was the toughest; it had to catch the eye and the interest, while indicating what was to follow. After a few false starts, the story emerged, in all its fascinating implications. David wrote until he had utilized most of his material, then put his work aside and went out to dinner. He still felt too close to the story to do any editing, so he took the subway uptown and went to a movie.

Wednesday morning, David read his story through and edited it ruthlessly. It was much too long (he had been aware of this while he was writing) but now he was able to separate the wheat from the chaff, balance the grotesque against the serious and select a wide enough variety of anecdotes to give breadth to the account.

After dinner, he retyped the manuscript, making minor grammatical corrections. Then he typed out a note:

"Dear Mr. Holloway, When I first came across the facts enclosed, I didn't believe them. They are, as you will see, quite true. If this is an old subject which has been amply covered before, I'm sorry. I checked our library and could find nothing there."

Then David signed his name, clipped the note to the story and slipped the sheaf of papers into a large envelope.

He left the Y a little earlier than usual the next afternoon and went up to the office. He dropped the envelope in the city editor's mailbox and departed.

☆☆☆ 9

DAVID GETS AN EXCLUSIVE

WHILE DAVID WAS not due at the shack until 6 p.m., he made it a practice to get there ahead of time. This gave him a chance to check the precinct across the street before calling his office to let them know he was on the job. His conversation with the desk lieutenant always began with, "Anything doing?"

"Nothing much," the desk officer responded this time. "We just got a call that a woman was found dead—apparently of natural causes—in her flat way over on the upper east side. The address is a poor one. It sounds like a cheap case. Nobody important from what I can gather. All I have is a name so far. Details ought to come in pretty soon."

It was a beautiful spring evening. Hanging around the shack· or in the precinct did not especially appeal to David. Besides, the other reporters hadn't come in yet. They weren't due for another fifteen minutes. And they might agree with the lieutenant, he'd have all the data on the phone soon.

This probably was, as the lieutenant said, an insignificant death—one that might be of no great newspaper reader interest, though it certainly would be of great moment to members of the family. But news-wise, it appeared as if it was worth a paragraph. It sounded like the sort of thing that happened every day in the year, especially in a big city. People were always dying.

"I'm going up to take a look," David said to the lieutenant. "I'll kill some time anyway."

David took the east side subway up and then changed to a bus, which took him to the address of the building in question. It was a dilapidated brownstone house and there was a crowd in front of it. There also were several police officers and an ambulance.

"Nothing much to it," a police sergeant who was in charge of the police detail said to David after the latter put his police card in his hat. "The medical examiner says there was nothing suspicious—cause of death was a stroke."

"Who found her?" David asked.

"Her husband."

David went into the building. Its walls were badly chipped. There was a small-watt bulb to "light" the way. He walked up to the second floor, elbowing his way around neighbors who were lining the steps. He had no trouble finding the apartment, since police were carrying the dead woman out.

David walked into the apartment. There sat the husband, dazed and dry-eyed. He was about thirty-five. Clinging to him was his daughter, three—his only child, it developed.

Gently and apologetically, David approached the man. It wasn't right to intrude on such private misery—but it had to be done.

"I'm terribly sorry," David said softly. "This is an awful thing. Had your wife been ill?"

"Never sick a day in her life. We were married eight years. We grew up together."

Then the man burst into sobs and cried, "Oh, my poor baby! What she must have been through!"

He carried on this way for ten minutes. Finally, he seemed

to gain control of himself and saw the inquiring look on David's face.

"I'm a salesman," the man began. "I was on the road for two weeks and came home this evening. What a homecoming!" he added bitterly. "I had had a wonderful trip—exceeded my quota. I was even thinking that a couple of more trips like this and we could move out of this neighborhood and maybe buy a house of our own.

"I came into the flat and what did I see—my wife dead in bed and little Theresa by her side.

" 'Mommy sleeping—*sshh,*' " the child said to me. 'She sleeping a long time.'

"The medical examiner who was just here estimates that my wife has been dead for about two days. For two days—do you hear? From what I can gather, Theresa has been foraging for herself all that time. The child never left the house, eating only what she could find in the kitchen and in the icebox.

"The neighbors said they never heard her cry. But for two days and nights in this small apartment with my dead wife! And thinking all the time 'mommy sleeping.' "

The police, of course, had most of these facts—but David was the only reporter at the scene—and time was beginning to run out for the first edition. While the police would give what details they had to the other reporters at the shack, David was the only one who had a personal interview with the stricken father—good, heart-rending quotes.

The first thing he did on leaving the apartment was to rush for a telephone to call his city desk and suggest that they send a photographer up. The story wound up with a two-column headline in a feature spot on the first page of the second section. With it went a picture—showing distraught father and child. The *Ledger* had by far the best story on the tragedy— and was the only paper to have a picture.

It was the day the story appeared that Bryan, the assistant

night city editor, gave David some good advice.

"That story of the dead mother worked out fine, David—and I'm glad you finally got one in. It was the best story on the split page.

"Don't ever get discouraged when you get a turn-down after offering a story. This doesn't mean you're to call on every insignificant thing that happens," he added hurriedly. "But let's put it this way: if you have any doubt at all, let the city desk decide.

"I want to warn you of something. Many of the boys on the other papers—and even some here, unfortunately—develop a pseudo-sophistication about stories. It gets to a point where the only story they'd get excited about would be an invasion of the city by Martians.

"The most important asset you bring to your job is enthusiasm—never forget that. A blasé reporter is his own worst enemy."

☆☆☆ 10

HIS FIRST BYLINE

ALMOST TWO WEEKS had gone by since David had submitted his feature on the "full mooners," and it was as though he had dropped it into a void. He was, of course, in constant touch with the city desk and once or twice even spoke with Holloway when the city editor had a question about a story David was giving in. But Holly was preoccupied at the time and somehow the opportunity to ask about his story didn't present itself. David had all but given up hope.

Then one Thursday night, when he reported for work at the shack, he found a penciled message on his desk, "Call Miss Rogers at the *Ledger,* extension 468."

David's visits to the *Ledger* were limited to his once-a-week stop-offs, when he picked up his pay check. It was now three months since he had become a district man, and he felt neither fish nor fowl on his brief visits to the city room. True, he was well above the rank of copy boy, but as a leg man (versus a writing reporter) he felt he was still a distance from attaining his goal.

"Who's Miss Rogers?" he mused. He was almost certain there was no female reporter named Rogers, yet it was hard to tell. In a newspaper as big as the *Ledger,* there were many specialized fields; there was a church reporter, who handled all religious stories, an education reporter—even a puzzle editor. They had little to do with the city desk.

Well, only one way to find out, thought David as he lifted the receiver and dialed the *Ledger's* number. "Extension 468 —oh, Suzy?"

"Yes, Davey—what's on your mind?"

"Listen, Suzy—who's Miss Rogers on extension 468?"

"That's Mark Cornish's secretary, you lucky lad. She's blonde, blue-eyed and not engaged. You dating her now?" Suzy had been a telephone operator at the *Ledger* for a long time. Very little went on of which she wasn't fully aware.

"I don't even know her, for heaven's sake! She called me and I'm calling back."

"Well, lucky you! She's busy now. You want to hold on or shall I call you back?"

"I'll hold on." As David waited, his puzzlement increased. Mark Cornish was the Sunday editor. The Sunday editor, as a rule, had very little to do with the city desk. He was in charge of a special section for Sunday readers which contained the week's review of the news, science and educational columns, special articles, features and items of a similar nature. To the best of his knowledge, David hadn't exchanged more than a half-dozen words with the Sunday editor since he had come to the *Ledger*. Why should his secretary . . . ?

His thoughts were broken into by a pleasant, feminine, "Hello."

"Hello, this is David White at the east side shack. You called me, Miss Rogers?"

"Yes, I did. You're the one who wrote the piece on the 'full mooners,' aren't you?"

Perplexed, David admitted his authorship, and Miss Rogers continued, "Mr. Cornish is going to run it in next Sunday's feature section, and he asked me to call and let you know." Her voice warmed considerably. "That's a fascinating article, Mr. White—I enjoyed it tremendously."

"Why—why thanks a lot," replied David. "But would you mind telling me how Mr. Cornish got it? I left it in Mr. Holloway's mailbox."

"I know. Every now and then when Holly has a feature piece which is good, and if news column space is tight, he'll send it along to Mr. Cornish for consideration in the Sunday section. Yours made the grade and you are doubly blessed; you'll receive a check for this and, in addition, it'll appear in the Sunday section, which has a far greater circulation than the weekday paper."

There was no reply for such a while that the girl's voice questioned, "Are you there? Hello?"

"Oh, I'm here," replied David heavily. "I'm just stunned."

They both laughed.

"Look," said David, "would you celebrate with me, Miss

Rogers? It's my first byline—and I'm just going to burst if someone isn't there to listen to me brag!"

"I wish I could." Her voice sounded really regretful. "But I'm leaving for my vacation tomorrow night, and I've a lot of packing to do. I know exactly how you feel—I felt the same way when I got this job last year. I'll take a rain check, if I may."

At the word "vacation," a bell rang with David.

"Come to think of it, I'm going on vacation myself in two weeks. Miss Rogers?"

"Alice," she prompted.

"Alice, can we postpone the celebration till I get back? You won't forget?"

"No," she laughed, "I won't forget, David."

"Have a good time, and thanks a million for calling, Alice. I'll see you in four weeks!"

"Don't thank me," replied Miss Rogers, "I seen my dooty and I done it." They both laughed and hung up.

David could have shouted for joy. However was he going to live until Sunday, when the deathless words "by David White" would jump out at him from the white newsprint!

Somewhat diffidently, he turned to Bill Baxter, who, under pretext of reading his book, had nevertheless not missed a trick.

"Bill?"

"Yep?"

"I think I'm going to have my first byline in Sunday's paper." The casual manner in which David tossed off the words didn't fool Baxter for one minute.

"No kidding!" The pride and warmth in the older man's voice was all the accolade David needed. "How you gonna live till Sunday?"

"I don't know," replied David truthfully.

11

VACATION TIME .

IN LATE AUGUST, David took his two weeks' vacation and went home for a brief reunion with his family.

It was good to be home again and back in the room he shared with his younger brother, Andrew. Andy was now seventeen, a full five years younger than David, and already an inch taller than his older brother. A year made a big difference in a boy's development, David found. Where he had said good-bye to a gangling, sixteen-year-old high-school sophomore, interested only in basketball and science-fiction comics, he returned home to a constantly ringing telephone and talk of dances, parties and "going steady."

A little taken-back at this turn of events, David sought out his mother, busy in the kitchen, and questioned her.

"What's this with Andy, Mom? When I left all he knew about girls was whether or not they could play basketball—and now all this talk of dates and 'going steady'—what goes on?"

Mrs. White, a small, intelligent woman with humorous eyes and a generous mouth, looked up at her older son and laughed.

"What a short memory you have! Andy's much better than you were. When you first discovered girls, I thought we'd have to skip a mortgage payment because of the laundry bills —you changed shirts at least four times a day. And I could never get to the hall mirror to put some lipstick on because you were rooted there, looking for your beard!"

David laughed defensively, "Oh, you're exaggerating."

"Maybe just a bit." His mother smiled affectionately. "You were a dilly, though." Her eyes took on a concerned look. "Davey, you look awfully pale. Doesn't the sun shine in New York?"

David smiled. "Last time I saw it, it sure did. But you know, Mom, I work when others sleep. I don't quit until two in the morning, and by the time I have a snack and get to my room, why, I don't get to sleep much before five or so."

"Then the day is more than half over when you wake up." Mrs. White sighed. "I'm not very happy about this arrangement, Davey. We didn't want to sound like wet blankets, so Dad and I never wrote you of our concern. But really—I don't like the idea of you wandering around a big city like New York in the dead of night. All sorts of strange people are out, and anything could happen to you. Although I must say," she added fondly, "that you know how to turn adversity to advantage! I'd have been petrified of those 'full mooners,' but you made a wonderful story out of them. Oh, Davey—we were so proud of you here! Dad showed the clipping to everyone at the laboratory.

"But I still don't like the idea of your wandering around the city by yourself," she added abruptly.

David leaned over and kissed the top of her head.

"You can stop worrying, Mom. Usually I'm in the safest place in the world—a police station! And you can just forget all those stories about the big, bad city—it's a good grade B movie plot, and that's about all. Mom—New York is just about the greatest—I can't begin to tell you. But I want you and Dad to try to come there for Christmas and let me show it to you. Just wait till you see it at Christmas time—the tree in Rockefeller Center towering over the statue of Prometheus and decorated with giant colored balloons—like a colossal candy tree!

"And the store windows on Fifth Avenue—you can't conceive of the imagination and richness of the Christmas display. And you don't just get pleasure in the wealth of the city . . . it's all over . . . wait till you see one of those huge ocean liners nosing into a pier on the Hudson River . . . or the odd sight of the kids ice-skating in Central Park against a background of towering skyscrapers."

Mrs. White had been regarding David closely during his outburst, and now she said, a little wistfully, "I was going to tell you, David, that you needn't feel you have burned your bridges behind you. That we would not in the least feel you had failed in any way if you changed your mind about working on the *Ledger* and decided to come home to stay."

David looked at his mother with surprise.

"Wherever did you get that idea? Mom, I wouldn't change places with the King of Siam! I love the city and I'm learning more about it every day. I just wish," he added a little morosely, "I could learn faster."

"Davey, don't sell yourself short," his mother brought him up firmly. "If I know you at all, I know you're giving the *Ledger* good value for your salary. If anything, you're too conscientious! Now," she led him out to the porch, "sit down and tell me all about your job."

"I wrote you all about it," David protested.

"Not what you wrote me about," said his mother understandingly. "I want the things you didn't write. For instance," she prompted with attempted casualness, "have you met any nice girls?"

David laughed. "Mom, you'll never change."

"I hope not," Mrs. White rejoined placidly. "But have you?"

"No, I haven't," David confessed. "It's these crazy hours. And most of the men who work with me are married. But really, I don't care. I keep busy, and besides, dating in New York is a pretty expensive deal."

"I'm sure all of the young people who go out on dates in New York are not millionaires," his mother retorted dryly. "However, I can see where your working hours would be quite a detriment to social activity." She shrugged. "Maybe your fortunes will change soon. I don't like to think of you going to the movies by yourself on your days off. It's a lonely business. Oh, well—everybody's going to be mighty hungry before long, so I'd better get busy." She rose from her chair.

"Off with you, boy. Go visit some old friends and dazzle them with your big-city sophistication!" She kissed him fondly and turned back into the kitchen.

In the course of the next week, David's father met him for lunch downtown twice and then brought him back to the pharmaceutical laboratory where he was employed, to meet some of his business friends.

"So this is the New York City reporter," said one of his father's colleagues as he was introduced.

David flushed. "Well, not really, but soon, I hope," he hastened to set the record straight.

David's visit home was over almost before he knew it. He wanted to get to New York a few days before he was due back at his job, so that he could concentrate on finding a small apartment, but somehow that plan didn't work out. A number of his home town friends had married and they had "booked" him for dinner on different nights.

He finally flew back to New York the very last day of his vacation.

12

DETECTIVE STORY

DAVID'S FIRST ACT when he returned to work at the shack was to call extension 468, at the *Ledger*. Fortunately, Alice Rogers had not yet left for the day. To her answering, "Hello," he replied, "It's David. Remember me?"

After some bantering conversation, they made a lunch date for the following afternoon at one, in the *Ledger* cafeteria, which was located on an upper floor of the newspaper building. Since they both knew the cafeteria quite well, they were able to single out the particular corner table in an uncrowded area at which they would meet, thus assuring some amount of privacy for this first date.

The conversation was brief, but very promising, and, after checking in with the city desk, David felt too elated just to sit around the shack, so he strolled across the street to renew his friendships at the precinct.

After greeting the lieutenant at the desk, David walked upstairs to where the "brains"—the detectives—had their office, in the room known as the squad room. Holding the fort all by himself for the moment was detective Terry Mulligan, who had been promoted to first grade detective only one month previously for capturing an armed thug who specialized in pistol-whipping hotel clerks and then robbing them in the early hours of the morning. David had handled the details of that arrest and he had been much taken with Mulligan—who looked like anything but a cop. As a matter of fact, David would have been hard put to it to give an accurate description of Mulligan, who had the wonderful asset (for a detective) of being virtually nondescript. . . . David had been introduced to him three separate times—and Mulligan took visible delight in the fact that each time the young reporter had recognized only the name.

The man was a human chameleon, David decided. The first time David met him, the detective was impeccably dressed in a dark gray business suit and he had a quietly urbane manner; he was at that time "tailing" a well-known confidence man whose recent activities were somewhat suspicious. The second time David met Mulligan, he mistook him for a prisoner. Each squad room had a section partitioned off as a temporary prison cell, in which especially rambunctious suspects were placed while being questioned. A number of surly teen-agers, wearing leather jackets and dirty sneakers, were being questioned on a charge of rifling parked cars, and a member of the group disengaged himself from the rest and walked around to the detectives' side. One of the latter started to introduce the newcomer, and, on second introduction, David realized with a start that the pugnacious-looking "teen-ager" was Terry Mulligan again!

The third time it happened, David was exchanging pleasantries with the lieutenant at the desk downstairs when two very sharply dressed men walked in. They were as alike in appearance and demeanor as peas in a pod—from the narrow charcoal suits to the tab-collared shirts. But even more similar than the clothing was the fastidious walk and the aloof manner. As they passed David on their way upstairs, one of the dudes winked broadly at him.

David turned mystified eyes on the lieutenant. "Society card sharp, probably. Or maybe a dope handler. Go on up and see." The reporter scuttled up the stairs as one of the "dandies" removed his coat. Once again, David was introduced to the man who had winked at him—Mulligan.

Now, temporarily "at liberty," Terry Mulligan sat completely relaxed, his feet up on the desk—a lean and wiry man who could have passed for twenty, though he was just about forty. His smile was open and friendly as he greeted David and motioned to him to sit down. "What's doing, boy?"

"That's what I came to ask you," replied David, approaching the chair. As he did so, he stumbled over some objects on the floor. Catching his balance, he looked down at a mess of cigar butts, ground-out cigarettes, burnt-out matches and ashes settling lazily again after being disturbed by his foot.

"Look," exclaimed David, exasperated, "please don't think I'm a fuss-budget, but we have lots of ash trays over at the shack—more than we need. All of you detectives here smoke —and there isn't a single ash tray in the place. Please let me make you a present of a few."

"Don't do us any favors," replied Mulligan promptly. "They're not here because we don't want them." He spoke with a vehemence which puzzled David.

"Don't jump to conclusions, boy," Mulligan smiled. "We'd just rather be dirty than dead."

At the bewildered look in David's eyes, the detective relented.

"A couple of years ago," he explained, "one of the detectives in this squad brought in a prisoner. I think the charge was felonious assault. The suspect had beaten somebody over the head with a baseball bat for no reason whatsoever.

"While being questioned by the arresting officer, this character suddenly picked up a six-inch glass ash tray from the desk and slammed it into the detective's face. The cop was in a bad way, I can tell you. He had a severe gash under one eye, and he's lucky he didn't lose it. He did manage to keep the prisoner from escaping.

"Ever since then, the rule in this precinct has been never

to have any ash trays around. Maybe it doesn't look neat, but it's a lot safer. Besides, we have a sweeper."

David whistled in surprise. "I had no idea they'd try stunts like that right in a station house!"

"A suspect will try anything, anywhere," replied Terry Mulligan flatly. "What've they got to lose? Once you make a pinch (arrest)—whether it's a hophead (drug addict) or a house man (burglar)—you stay alive only if you stay alert. I could tell you stories . . ."

"Why don't you?" prompted David.

Mulligan laughed. "What's the matter? Are things that dull?"

"Kind of," admitted David. "And sometimes it's tough as pulling hen's teeth to get a complete story out of this precinct. About three weeks ago I wanted to get some details on an arrest from detective Brady, and he almost bit my head off."

"Look, Dave—let me explain something to you. If there was nothing to being a detective but just the detecting alone—outfiguring, outsmarting and outmaneuvering a suspect—the job would be a snap. You know what breaks your back in this job? The paper work! Sometimes a case won't break until maybe ten minutes before you're due to be relieved and then you're stuck for hours at the precinct. Doing what? Paper work! And no overtime pay, either.

"Brady probably gave you the brush-off because he was detained just that way. Maybe he and his wife were supposed to go to a show or something and he got stuck shoving a pencil. And then you come along to take up more time!"

"But I have a job to do, too," asserted David firmly.

"I know." Mulligan smiled understandingly. "Tell you what, Dave. You let me know if any of the boys give you a hard time. I can't promise anything, but I'll try."

"I'd appreciate that," replied David. "I know I could go to the lieutenant, who could order Brady to give me the information; but I don't like a strained relationship."

"It isn't the happiest kind," agreed Mulligan. "I myself prefer to give a break and get a break. Works out fine, usually. I made a good pinch just last week on that basis."

"Oh?" David searched his mind rapidly. His father, of course, subscribed to the *Ledger,* and he had read the paper thoroughly at home during his vacation. And all this afternoon he had gone through the papers for the last few days. The only recent local crime story of any importance was a burglary arrest. "Did you have that burglary in the east sixties?"

"That's the one," replied Mulligan with satisfaction. "And I'm still recuperating."

Whereupon the detective proceeded to give David the lowdown:

"About two or three years ago, I picked up a nineteen-year-old kid on a charge of carrying a revolver. While the kid was no angel—as a matter of fact, he was hanging around with a real tough bunch—he had never committed a serious crime. This was the first time that a felony rap could have been hung on him.

"Well, you know—felony's no joke. He would've been finished for life. So I put some time in, looking him over— talked with his parents, his old teachers, the neighbors. From what I learned, I decided to take a chance on him.

"Anyway, the kid was arraigned in court and found guilty. The judge asked the assistant district attorney who prosecuted the case to make a recommendation on sentence, and then the d.a. read into the court record the statement I gave him. On the basis of that, the kid got a suspended sentence.

"I told him to keep his nose clean and if I ever found him in any more trouble, I would personally kick him from here to Brooklyn. He swore that he was finished with the gang, and that if he could ever do anything for me, he would.

"Well, you know how those things are. If good wishes could

pay bills, I'd have had a trip to Florida a long time ago!

"Anyway, about a month ago, out of a clear sky, the kid called me up. He wasn't in trouble, but he had some information. Incidentally," Mulligan interrupted his story, "here's something you should know. Much of a detective's success depends on what tips he gets—'information.' Often this information comes from somebody who has been in trouble and is treated right by members of the force. Call them stool pigeons or 'stoolies' or whatever, but I can tell you off the record that ninety per cent of the good arrests made in this town come from 'information'!"

Mulligan paused to let that sink in, then continued.

"The kid was in a bar one night and he was approached by a middle-aged man who struck up a conversation. The man put away almost a quart of hard stuff and then began bragging in a vague sort of way about how he was driving the cops crazy with some burglaries.

"The kid gave me a fine description of the man, even to the fact that on his left wrist he had a small tattoo of a pierced heart with the name 'Mary.'

"Well, as a matter of fact, we surely had been going nuts with a series of burglaries. People who had been away for week ends were calling the precinct with complaints of jewelry and silver missing. We had our hands full, I can tell you!

"So I talked it over with the lieutenant and got assigned to this case full time.

"For a week, I haunted the tavern where the kid had met the man, and, sure enough, on the seventh day the guy with the tattoo shows up. He wasn't making any conversation, so I had to put him to bed."

"Put him to bed?" parroted David.

"Tailed him to his home," explained Mulligan. "I followed him—from a distance and without his observing me, of course —and he finally wound up in a cheap rooming house.

"For a month I lived with the guy—ate breakfast, lunch and dinner with him, usually about eight tables removed, and with a newspaper in front of my face.

"The last couple of nights I finally got some action. He started going into the service entrances of a number of swank apartment houses and jimmying the doors of several apartments."

"Is that when you made the arrest?" asked David.

"No, I wanted him red-handed. And I knew now it was just a question of another day or so. Sure enough, I was 'walking him' the next night when he passed a brownstone duplex. He cased the place, found a partially open window and climbed in. On his way out, he looked considerably fatter, so I made the pinch. Sure enough, he had on him some priceless antique silver, plus a couple of diamond brooches, earrings and a matched pearl necklace.

"Down at the station house, he finally confessed to those other burglaries which were driving us crazy, so that cleaned the books up some."

David had a sudden thought. "Tell me," he asked, "what sort of outfits did you wear while you were following him?"

Mulligan laughed. "All of them," he teased. "Tell you one thing," he grew serious, "I couldn't have stood that guy for much longer. He was nuts for that hot Spanish food. Two, three nights a week he went into a little Mexican restaurant that specializes in tortillas and enchiladas. Darn near burned a hole in my stomach!" he added morosely.

"We must suffer for our art," quipped David. Then he added, "Look, Terry—this has the makings of a good yarn. I don't know if my paper is interested, or if anything will come of it—but I'd like to try. If you don't mind, that is?"

The detective extended his hand, palm up in supplicating fashion.

"Be my guest!" he replied.

☆☆☆ *13*

ALICE ROGERS

AT TEN MINUTES before one the next afternoon, David picked up a cup of coffee at the counter and proceeded to the specified corner table of the *Ledger's* cafeteria. With his newspaper propped against the sugar bowl in front of him, he attempted to look completely engrossed—to discourage any possible passers-by other than the one expected.

A yawn escaped him, and he smothered it quickly. He had had very little sleep last night, thanks to Terry Mulligan, for, although he had left the precinct shortly after the detective finished his narrative, David was fascinated with the story. Having seen Mulligan in action, so to speak, he could well imagine the various disguises the jaunty detective must have worn during his month-long surveillance.

It had been a dull night, news-wise, at the shack, so David had spent the time mapping out an article on the background of the burglary pinch, with emphasis on the chameleonlike qualities of the astute detective. In deference to Mulligan's "off the record" request, he had omitted all mention of the boy who had given him the tip, referring to that phase of the investigation as "acting on information"—a euphemism which is used by all newspapers. (But only now did David fully understand what the phrase meant.)

Back in his room at the Y, the article was still too alive in his mind to be stilled by sleep, so he took his typewriter out and went to work. Within ten minutes, there was a knocking on the wall and, muttering with frustration, he regretfully left the typewriter, set his alarm for nine and went to bed. "My number one project for this week," he thought, "an apartment!"

He was up before the alarm went off and, still in pajamas, attacked the story. He had it finished, edited and retyped by noon. He had shaved and dressed hurriedly, and now here he was.

"Hello!" A loaded tray was put down next to his newspaper and he looked up into a pair of blue eyes ringed with thick brown lashes, set in a heart-shaped face. He stumbled to his feet.

"Hello! Say—why'd you go and do that?" he indicated her filled tray.

"Oh, don't be silly—that's nothing. You can get dessert for both of us later, if you like. It's just that they were almost out of the roast-beef hash and I wanted to get it while the getting was good. Otherwise, I'd have been stuck with the pork chop. Ever have the pork chop here?"

David laughed. "I know what you mean." He looked at her closely. She was a remarkably pretty girl; blonde hair, cut almost as short as his—but with what a difference! Other than lipstick, she appeared to be devoid of make-up. Her brown eyebrows were slightly heavier than was currently fashionable, but he decided that gave her face character.

"Aren't you going to sit down?" she asked.

He hadn't even realized he was still standing and, coloring slightly, he slid back into his seat. "It's your own fault," he told her. "You shouldn't look like that."

Alice pointed to his half-empty coffee cup. "Is that all you're having? You'll make me feel like a glutton. Go and get some decent food."

Obediently, he arose and headed for the counter. Returning in a few minutes with some toast and scrambled eggs, he was struck with the odd happiness he felt on rejoining her. "Alice," he said hesitantly, "I can't help what this is going to sound like, but please believe me: I am so happy to know you!"

The blue eyes were discerning and quizzical as they met his. "David," she replied gently, "you're just lonesome and glad to have met a presentable and sympathetic female. I understand it, and I won't take undue advantage of it. O.K.? Now," she continued briskly, "what have you been writing since you did the 'full mooners'?"

"A piece on an unusual detective." David checked himself. "Say I didn't come here to talk about me—I came to find out about you!"

"We have plenty of time to find out about me," she retorted. "What about that detective? Have you written it?"

David gave her a brief outline on Mulligan and then mentioned that, now that the piece was written, he didn't know whether to submit it to Holloway or to her boss, Sunday editor Mark Cornish.

"Offer it to Holloway," advised Alice. "He's the man you're trying to please. If for any reason he can't use it, and it has merit, he'll send it along to Cornish."

Since that was pretty much the way David felt, too, he was glad to drop the matter and turn to more personal things. He told Alice about his room at the Y and how difficult it was to do any work there. "I'd like to get an apartment of my own," he concluded.

"Why don't you put a notice up on the bulletin board?" asked Alice. "You never know—people get married and give up small apartments, reporters get sent to other cities. Anyway, what have you got to lose?"

"Gee, that's a good idea! I wonder why I never thought of it," replied David. "May I use your typewriter after lunch?"

Alice nodded assent, after which the two young people exchanged a few biographical notes. Alice was one of those rare things—a native New Yorker—and she loved her city. She was profoundly relieved to discover that David echoed her sentiments. "If you had turned out to be one of those people who said, 'It's a wonderful town to visit but I wouldn't live there if you paid me,' well, I'd—well, I don't know what I'd do!" she declared.

"Remind me to say it some time and find out," said David, and they both laughed.

Suddenly it was almost two o'clock and Alice had to hurry. David took the elevator down to the fourth floor with her and escorted her to her desk. She put a sheet of copy paper in her typewriter and motioned to him to use it. He quickly typed out a notice to the effect that he would like to sublet or lease a small apartment in Manhattan with a nominal rent and added his phone number at the shack. Then he pulled the sheet out of the machine and turned to Alice.

"How about Saturday afternoon? I'm yours till six, when duty calls. We could do the museums, the park, a movie or what have you."

He looked down at her and suddenly realized she was smaller than he had thought—a maximum of five feet four, even in those heels. She seemed to sense his thoughts and looked up at him humorously.

"David," she said, "I just want to warn you about something. If you ever use the word 'cute' in describing me—everything is off between us. You understand?"

"Oh, now I get the pitch," he replied. "A *femme fatale!*"

"That's it. Now, scoot. I've work to do. About Saturday— do you know Biedermeyers', on Central Park East? It has a canopy out front and they serve those delicious pastries?" David nodded. "I've some shopping to do Saturday morning, and I'll be in that area. Suppose I meet you there about one? Fine!"

David turned and walked over to one side of the city room,

near the water cooler, where the bulletin board was located. He carefully folded over his notice, then neatly tore the excess paper from it and thumbtacked it to the board.

He glanced about the city room. Holloway was at his desk and did not appear too busy. David decided to beard the lion and approached the city editor.

"Hello, Mr. Holloway."

The perceptive gray eyes peered up at him from under the shaggy brows and noted the new assurance and poise of the former copy boy.

"Hello, my boy," boomed Holly, extending his hand. "How was your vacation? Anything new in Indiana?" David marveled that, with fifty or more people under him, the city editor was still able to remember who was vacationing, when and where!

"Not much," replied David, grinning. "Our circulation is up two, there. My father got two of his cronies to subscribe."

"It all helps." Holly laughed. "Say, that was an amusing piece on the 'full mooners.' Too bad I didn't have room for it myself—but I suppose you're not sorry." This was a reference to the fact that David had received a check because the article had appeared in the Sunday section.

"To tell you the truth, Mr. Holloway, it was my first byline —and I think I would almost have paid to get it in!"

Holly laughed aloud. Then, passing his hand over his short, gray hair, he asked, "Doing anything else much these days?"

"Well," replied David, "I had an interesting conversation with an unusual detective yesterday. It—almost wrote itself," he added lamely, taking an envelope from his pocket and placing it on Holly's desk.

Holloway plucked the copy from the envelope, skimmed over the first paragraph and then put it down on his desk. "I'll look it over later and let you know," he promised.

As David smiled his thanks and turned to go, Holly called

him back.

"Dave," he said enigmatically, "don't be too surprised if things start moving a little faster for you. I always did like enterprise—especially if it also harbors talent." He turned to pick up a phone. "See you," he said in parting.

Mystified, David walked toward the elevator.

☆☆☆ *14*

DAVID ALMOST COMES TO THE END

IT WAS A FEW NIGHTS later that David's newspaper career almost came to a sudden end.

He was reading an afternoon newspaper—he read all of the city's newspapers, to see how they handled similar stories—when the *Ledger's* phone in the shack rang. David grabbed it, even before the first ring was completed.

"We got a tip that some neighbor has found what appears to be a murdered man at the Triangle Apartments," Johnny Sampson, one of the assistants on the city desk, told David. "We even have the apartment number—3C. Take a look and call us back. It's only a couple of blocks from your shack."

"Right," David said. "I'll hop right on it."

David mentioned the tip to the other reporters in the shack, but he had no takers. Baxter said he had a headache, and the other two felt, if there was anything to the story, they could pick up all the details from the precinct in plenty of time.

David hustled out. He already knew that if there were anything to this tip, the chances were good that the police would

be there already. He thought of crossing the street to the precinct and inquiring at the lieutenant's desk about the report
phoned in to the *Ledger,* but decided against it.

"Heck," David said to himself, "it's only two blocks away.
I might as well walk over. I'm tired of sitting and reading anyway."

He hurried toward the apartment house. If this tip turned
out to be true, it could make a good story, especially since
there were some fairly well known people living in that building. Besides, he only had about twenty minutes to call the
desk, get a rewrite man and feed him the information—if any.

David took the elevator to the third floor of the apartment
house. He looked around and found 3C—the third door on
the left of the self-service elevator.

There appeared to be no police activity and nobody was in
the darkened hallway. He rang the bell of the apartment. No
response. He pressed harder on the button. It was a louder
ring this time. Still no answer.

He was about to return to the elevator when he decided to
try the door knob. He turned it gently. The door opened easily.
It had been closed—but not locked.

"What do I do now?" David asked himself. "There may be
a murdered man in there. If so, where is everybody?"

David pushed the door open and walked in. It was pitch
black. Not a single light was on in the apartment. He groped
around and found an electric switch in the foyer. It was a
tastefully furnished apartment and everything seemed in order.
He looked into the adjacent kitchen. There was a slight hum
from the refrigerator. Nothing was disarranged there either.
He walked—slowly—toward the rear of the apartment, ill at
ease and apprehensive.

Suddenly, he thought he heard a slight moan from the bedroom. Now he was just plain scared, but he had to see it
through. The bedroom was dark—and there was no telling

where the switch might be. He almost tripped over a slipper. The moan grew louder.

David, his heart beating a mile a minute, groped for the light switch along the wall, found it—and flicked on the lights.

There on the bed lay an elderly man, gasping for breath. His right clenched fist was pressed against the center of his chest, as if he were in severe agony. The man saw David—but seemed to have lost the power of speech. His mouth opened and he attempted to speak—but nothing came out.

"What's the trouble—what happened?" David called out to the man, who seemed paralyzed.

"Doc-tor," the man managed to gasp. "Doc-tor. Heart."

David wheeled about and ran to the foyer of the apartment, where he recalled having seen a telephone when he entered.

As he was about to pick up the instrument, a policeman burst into the apartment. His .38-caliber service revolver was in his right hand. He pointed it directly at David's head.

"Don't move or you're dead!"

David couldn't have moved, even if he had wanted to. He was frozen in his tracks. The officer frisked him thoroughly and expertly, patting the front and back of his coat and his trouser pockets.

"I'm a reporter," David finally managed to blurt out, after standing at attention for what seemed like an eternity. "My name is David White. I work for the *Ledger.*"

"Let's see your press card!" the patrolman demanded, lowering the gun a little and moving about a foot away from his "prisoner," not taking his eyes off him for a fraction of a second. In his left hand the officer held his nightstick—which looked almost as menacing as the black revolver with the pearl handle.

David shook violently as he fumbled for the press card in his oversized wallet, which was fattened with clippings of stories he had covered. The patrolman kept pointing what looked—to David, anyway—like a cannon. Finally, David found his press card and showed it to the patrolman.

"What are you doing here?" the officer demanded, after examining the press card minutely. "We got a call that a man had been murdered in this apartment. Where's the *corpus delicti?*"

David, pale and still shaken, led the patrolman to the bedroom. The man in the bed was moaning, quietly.

"Doc-tor," he cried weakly as he saw the officer.

The policeman ran for the phone. Within a few minutes, a police emergency truck—carrying the hundreds of different pieces of equipment necessary to meet almost any type of emergency—responded, as did a city ambulance. After the man was fed oxygen, he was removed to a hospital. Despite the unnerving experience still uppermost in his thoughts, David could still marvel at the speed and efficiency of the Emergency Service Police—and at the paradox of those huge hamlike hands, which were so incredibly gentle.

It developed that the man had suffered a heart attack and was unable to move. But a neighbor, who had heard his weak cries from an adjacent bedroom, somehow assumed that the man—who lived alone—was being beaten to death. A faithful reader of the *Ledger,* he had called the paper even before calling the police.

Back in the shack, David skipped the personal details in reporting his findings to the newsmen there. "There was nothing to the tip. It was a phoney." Then he buried his head in a newspaper. He was still too unnerved to discuss it.

"You did two things wrong," detective Terry Mulligan scolded the next night, when David related his demoralizing experience.

"First of all, you had no right to enter a strange apartment on your own. You are not a police officer, you know, though I am sure your intentions were of the best. I don't mind telling you that I've bumped into some reporters who think laws were not made for them.

"Second—and even more important—you should have been wearing your press card outside, where the policeman could not possibly miss it. It does you no good in your wallet."

David felt sheepish, recalling similar advice from the police officer at Jackson Airport.

"You were extremely lucky that that cop wasn't trigger happy," continued Mulligan. "It happened to be Charley Crimmins, who only has six months to go for twenty years in the job, when he becomes eligible for retirement at half pay. I think he once killed a man who tried to get away from him.

"Had Crimmins shot you, you would have had no recourse. You had gone into somebody else's apartment without permission—and since the officer had been told to check on a suspected homicide, he could well have mistaken you for a murderer."

From that time on, David kept his press card in an easily accessible spot in his wallet—and he did not hesitate to wear it on assignments.

The following Monday was a red-letter day for David. It marked his second byline. Sunday had been an unusually dull news day and, obviously, there had been ample space, for there on the split page was his story on Terry Mulligan. He read it through intently, noting where minor changes had been made. They were comparatively few, however, for David was learning his trade well. He had a nice, light touch and a good command of the language—two vital assets for a writing reporter.

When he had seen Alice Rogers on Saturday, she had told

him the Mulligan piece had not yet been channeled to Cornish.

"That means one of two things," said David gloomily. "Either Holly plans to use it himself, or, more likely, he's thrown it out."

"Don't be such a pessimist," chided Alice.

When they finished lunch, they went walking through the park, ablaze now with autumn colors. He told her of his close call in the apartment of the man with the heart attack and was oddly happy at the genuine concern she evinced.

Alice phoned David at the Y Monday morning and woke him up.

"Well, Gloomy Gus?" she greeted him.

Since David always bought the paper the previous night, he knew to what she was referring. "Isn't it wonderful?" he crowed sleepily. "I've got to call Mulligan—he'll get a kick out of it."

"I don't know about Mulligan—but I got a kick out of it myself. Just thought I'd let you know."

David rolled out of bed and headed for the shower.

Ten minutes later, he dialed Mulligan's home phone. The detective answered himself and instantly recognized David's voice.

"Hey, Dave?" his voice sounded boyish and jubilant. "My phone hasn't stopped ringing since last night. I'm a celebrity."

"Really?" said David. "I just wondered whether you'd seen the piece."

"Not only did I see it—but all my relatives and half the police department did. Usually we have to push the kids out the door to get them to school on time. This morning they were dressed and breakfasted by eight. Each bought a copy of the *Ledger,* and I can just imagine how they're going to carry on at school!" He laughed aloud.

"Well, gee," said David, pleased, "I'm glad it's worked out

this way."

"It worked out fine," said Mulligan, a bit more soberly. "You didn't hoke it up and you stuck to the facts. A nice story like that isn't going to do me any harm downtown, and it might even do me some good. Any time I can return the favor, don't hesitate."

"That's all right, Terry. I'm glad we're both happy."

When David stopped by the *Ledger* office to pick up his pay check the following Thursday, he waited until things looked comparatively quiet at the city desk and then walked over to Holloway.

"I'm glad you liked the Mulligan story."

"Eh?" Holloway looked up from a sheaf of copy paper in front of him. "Oh, hello there, Dave! Yes, that wasn't a bad piece. That's a real eager beaver detective there. A friend of yours?"

"I hope so," replied David. "I mean, apart from the fact that he can be of real value to me—I like him. He's a very nice guy."

"Fine!" boomed Holloway. "It's a good idea to have friends in the right places. Never know when they can be of help. Got any more stories?" he prodded.

"A couple of ideas," admitted David with a smile.

"Be glad to see them," replied Holly, returning to the papers on his desk.

As David started to walk off, Holly remembered something. "Dave?"

"Yes?" David turned back.

"Mulvaney tells me he hasn't had to yell at you in a long time," said Holloway with a twinkle. "He's really the acid test, you know. Once a leg man pleases Mulvaney, it's a sure sign he knows his business. Just thought I'd let you know."

"Thanks," replied, David deeply pleased.

☆☆☆ *15*

FIRES AND FIREBUGS

EVER SINCE THE JACKSON AIRPORT catastrophe, David
had unconsciously veered away from the thought of fires. This
was not an easy thing to do, since there was a fire house just
across the street from the shack, right next to the precinct, and
the fire bells were easily audible when he was at work. Also,
there was a master Fire Department ledger in the shack. This
gave the location of each ring.

For instance, the fire alarm box at the big city hospital on
the east side—about a mile from the fire station—carried the
number 763. Should an alarm be pulled from that box, that
number would ring in at the fire station—a set of seven con-
secutive rings, followed after a short break by a series of six
rings, followed by another short break and then a series of
three rings—763.

Consequently, every time David heard the bells ring in the
fire house, he would scan the ledger to see what fire box had
been pulled. He soon realized that, should a box like 763 ring
in, you rolled with the engines—that is, you hopped a cab
and got to the hospital as fast, almost, as the engine and hook
and ladder companies.

"A one-alarm fire—or a one-bagger as we call it—in a hospital," a veteran fireman explained to David, "automatically
brings out a lot more fire equipment than a one-alarm in practically any other place.

73

"The Fire Department realizes that the lives of crippled and bedridden people are at stake—and we take no chances. We roll in strength. And if we don't get that fire under control within a few minutes, a second and third alarm are rung in, bringing out additional equipment."

In one respect, however, a fire differed from almost every other type of disastrous happening—and that was in the tremendous crowds which always collected. Although most people are notoriously curious and crowd around at every kind of accident, they congregate almost literally in hordes at fires, David learned.

They made everybody's job that much harder—the fireman's, the policeman's and the reporter's.

It was especially tough when the origin of the fire was suspect. For if the fire was set off by an arsonist, the odds were excellent that the firebug was somewhere in the front line of spectators.

Covering a fire, David soon realized, was a very difficult business. Often a fire spread over a considerable area, and it was impossible for one or even a group of reporters to see what was going on, especially at a smoky fire.

And then the fire buffs were no help, either.

These were a group of men who were just crazy for fires. Many of them owned short-wave radios on which they were able to tune in on the Fire Department radio channel and learn about practically every fire in the city. The bigger the fire, the more fire buffs would show up.

Once there, they delighted in "helping" the firemen lug the heavy rubber hose lines—until some officer would tell them to get out of the way. This did not deter them in the least, and many would attempt to ingratiate themselves by running for coffee for the firemen during a break while fighting a blaze.

While the fire buffs seemed to know all the technical terminology, such as the specific type of pumpers that the fire engines were using on various fires, they often got in David's way and were considered a swift pain in the neck by most reporters.

The fire marshal, or one of his deputies, was the one, David found, who could fill him in on the facts concerning the fire. A deputy marshal—or at big fires the chief marshal himself—had to respond on every conflagration, regardless of size. This, David realized, was to check for possible arson, and marshals were trained to look for the exact cause of each fire.

"Arsonists are a strange breed," a deputy fire marshal said to David at one fire which was believed to be suspicious. "They don't set fires necessarily because they hate anybody; they just get a thrill out of seeing flames and an even bigger thrill out of hearing the sirens and watching the engines speeding through the streets.

"Also, the odds are good that they are right in the vicinity of the fire when the fire equipment arrives. The records show there have been numerous instances where the firebug himself has run up, as the fire engines responded, to say, 'I turned in the alarm!'

"They don't volunteer the information, of course, that they also set the fire—that little chore is left for us to uncover."

There was something about this information that appealed to David and he decided to look into it further. If the facts warranted it, there might be an interesting feature in fires and the aberrations of those who ignite them.

And so David phoned and made an appointment to interview the fire marshal the following Tuesday at 2 p.m.

The fire marshal, Frederick Taylor, turned out to be a Hoosier boy who had come to the big city in his youth, and at one time thought of taking up journalism as a career. Somehow, he got diverted, went to work for an insurance company as an adjuster and specialized in checking fire insurance claims. When an opening developed in the city fire marshal's office, he took the civil service examination and passed with a high grade. He had now been in the city fire marshal's office for nineteen years, the last five as the chief fire marshal.

While he tried hard to be an affable "regular guy" during the interview, he was obviously nervous and spoke in a stilted fashion.

"How can I help you?" asked Marshal Taylor, who had always received a good press because of his willingness to speak to newspapermen, even when he was routed out of bed in the middle of the night.

David explained that he would like to do a feature story on arsonists.

"You couldn't have come to a better place," the fire marshal said. "We get all kinds here."

With a good deal of prompting, the marshal finally launched into a detailed account of how his office had assigned eight deputy marshals to track down the cause of a series of fires in elementary schools in the last six months.

"What confounded us," the marshal said, "was that at first these fires were in just one area. We were almost certain that it was being done by somebody who lived in that general vicinity.

"We were all set to pounce on an elderly man whom we had seen go in and out of these schools, when suddenly fires started to break out in schools several miles away. And mind you, these new fires were occurring while we were tailing this suspect.

"It turned out that the man we were suspicious of was not involved at all. The fires were being set by members of a gang of young hoodlums—and in order to get into this gang, prospective members were forced to prove their mettle by setting fires. And in schools, of all places."

"Do you know the boys who set these fires?" David asked.

"Yes, I do. But they were all under sixteen. And I can't give the names to you, because, as you know, under the law of this state, a boy under sixteen is considered a minor and his name cannot be given out for publication. The theory is that such a young boy is considered salvageable—and if he were identified in the newspapers, it could do him irreparable harm. About the only exception I know to that rule is when a person under sixteen commits a murder. Otherwise, they are all arraigned in Children's Court, where the proceedings are secret and even the press is barred."

David spent almost two hours with the fire marshal, and in some respects it was tough sledding, for, while the official was willing enough, he was a nervous man and the sight of the young reporter's pencil seemed to paralyze his tongue. Fortunately, David was astute enough to recognize this and halfway through the interview he put his pencil and paper away. With a small prayer for powers of total recall, he sat back in his chair and conducted the interview along the lines of a pleasant, amiable chat.

The marshal relaxed visibly, and David directed the conversation toward the various types of firebugs, their highly individual methods and foibles.

When David felt he could not possibly remember any more, he thanked the marshal and left. All the way back to the Y, on the subway, he made notes, and he continued to do this in his room until he had exhausted his memory. That would fix it, he felt. When the piece was finished, he could check those things he was uncertain of over the phone.

Now that his notes were complete, David looked around the room and once again felt irritated with its impersonal, hygienic look.

Annoyed with himself, he got up and put on his coat. It was almost 6 p.m. and twilight was settling over the city.

"I've tried every other means of getting an apartment—asking every one, reading the ads and putting a notice up on the bulletin board. Now I think I'll try some old-fashioned leg work."

With that, he stalked out, his coat collar up to head off the chill February wind and headed, almost as though by instinct, to an area in the city of which he was particularly fond.

☆☆☆ *16*

AN APARTMENT FOR HIS OWN CASTLE

THIS NEIGHBORHOOD OF NEW YORK that David loved was included within about four blocks north and south and two blocks east and west, in Greenwich Village. This limited area seemed to him like a small town.

Aside from a very few apartment buildings, there were nothing but old brownstone houses with high stoops. A number of trees were dotted along each block—little trees, which fought for their very lives in the asphalt pavement. There were few stores. David passed a small tailor shop; farther along he saw a small art shop with well-known reproductions in the window. At the corner was a delicatessen.

As David advanced, he ignored the apartment houses, but he looked closely at the windows of the brownstones. Most of these, he knew, were known as "floor throughs"—that is, there was one apartment on each floor, running from front to back. Wherever he saw no signs of tenancy—no shades or blinds or curtains of any sort—he stopped and made inquiry.

He had covered about five blocks with no success whatever and had just about decided that his idea was ridiculous when,

desperately, he decided to try one last house. In this particular brownstone, there was a light on every floor but the top
one.

"I beg your pardon," he said to the elderly woman who answered his ring, "but would you know whether there was an
apartment available in this building?"

"If that isn't the queerest thing!" replied the woman. "Why
did you ask that?"

"Well, I noticed the top floor is dark," replied David. "Is
there?"

"There is—as of five minutes ago." The woman laughed.
"It hasn't been occupied for the past two months. The young
man who lived there was recently transferred to Chicago. He
wasn't sure he'd like it there, so he held onto this apartment.
Well, he only just called me to tell me he liked Chicago fine—
as a matter of fact, he's getting married there."

David wanted to pinch himself to make sure he wasn't
dreaming.

"Could I see it, please?" he asked.

"Yes, of course. I was just about to write an ad for the
newspaper. It's rather small," she warned him as she led the
way up the stairs.

At the top of the third flight, she opened the door and
switched on the light. "Well, here it is," she said.

David looked about him. The ceilings slanted, like those of
the attic at home. That meant it would probably be a little
warm in the summer. But otherwise it was a fair-sized room,
nicely decorated. A couch covered with a plaid material
placed near the window was obviously the bed as well. There
were a number of bookcases, painted the same light blue as the
walls, two easy chairs and a small desk.

The woman walked inside ahead of David and switched on
the light in a small alcove, to the left. "Here's your kitchen and
bath," she said. It was a tiny kitchenette, with a two-burner

stove and a small refrigerator. The bathroom was opposite the kitchen, adequate and clean.

"May I open a window?" David asked, and, as the woman nodded, he proceeded to do so. He looked out into the street he had just left. The building opposite was a few feet lower than this one and, as a result, there was an unobstructed breeze.

"How much is the rent here?" David asked.

The woman mentioned a sum which, while it was higher than he had expected, was not completely out of the question.

"Look—could you hold this for me for a few hours? I'd like to have a friend of mine see it, and she won't be through work before seven."

"Of course, but don't you rush into anything like a lease without giving it full thought. Besides, I haven't even started to compose the ad for the newspaper, so I won't be losing any tenants. You run along and meet your lady and bring her here. My name is Mrs. Halley."

"I'm David White, Mrs. Halley, and I work for the *Ledger*. Thanks a lot for your trouble. We'll see you shortly after seven."

David raced around the corner to a drugstore and dashed for the telephone booth. He dialed the *Ledger* and asked for extension 468.

"Alice?" He had to restrain himself to keep from shouting. "Can you get out early? I think I've found an apartment, and I want you to see it!"

Alice was rather busy at the moment, so the conversation was brief. He was to pick her up at the *Ledger;* she would come with him and see the apartment and then they would have dinner.

He spent the intervening hour just walking around the neighborhood. After all, he reasoned, if he was going to live there, he might as well know where the nearest laundry was, the small restaurants and other services. For while he knew the area, his interest now was far more personal.

Finally, because he still had time to spare, he took a bus uptown. The bus was snagged in the heavy, late afternoon traffic and Alice was waiting in front of the *Ledger* building when he finally arrived there.

"I'm sorry," David apologized. "Every time I take a bus I make a mental note never to take one again—and then I forget and do it!"

"Never mind," said Alice. "I'm dying to see the apartment! Have you taken it yet?" She accompanied him down the subway stairs.

"No, I wanted you to see it first. It's one large room, and a small kitchen and bath. But it looks so comfortable!" There was such longing in David's voice that Alice laughed.

"I don't know what you want me to see it for—if I didn't like it, you'd never forgive me!"

"You'll like it," he promised.

And she did. As they walked down the quiet street Alice said, "I've always loved this neighborhood—it's so charming and peaceful, and only ten minutes from the heart of town." Alice lived with her parents on the upper west side, and it took her a good half hour to get to the *Ledger*.

Mrs. Halley answered David's ring almost immediately and preceded the young couple up the stairs. David said nothing; he was watching Alice with amazement as that young lady methodically tested every piece of furniture in the room. She pulled at the drawers to see whether they stuck, sat on each of the chairs in turn, and then the sofa-bed. She turned the lamps on and off, walked into the kitchenette and peered into the refrigerator, poked around in the bathroom and then came out and gave her verdict.

"Grab it," she whispered succinctly to David.

He sighed with relief. "Mrs. Halley," he said, "you have a

new tenant."

"Good!" she replied. "I'm glad you brought someone to
help you make up your mind . . . and someone who looks
beyond her nose. Young lady," Mrs. Halley addressed herself
to Alice, "you're much too pretty to have so much common
sense!"

David signed the lease in Mrs. Halley's living room. He
wanted to move in that very night but Alice dissuaded him.

"I'm pretty sure you can borrow my dad's car tomorrow and
do everything at your leisure, instead of killing half the night
with cabs. Besides, I'm hungry."

They ate in an inexpensive Italian restaurant, about two
blocks from the apartment, and talked, as usual, about the
Ledger, and the people who worked on it.

It was now almost a year since David had first entered the
shack and a little more than six months since he first began
dating Alice. They had hit it off from the start and he was
completely at ease with her. She had a keen and observing
mind and, while most of the *Ledger* people she spoke about
were little more than names to David, nevertheless, he was
kept well up on office doings.

The *Ledger* was peopled by queer ducks, even as was every
other large organization. There was Cameron Grayson, the
assistant Sunday editor, who ate pencils. "Well, he doesn't
really eat them—he just chews on them till they snap and then
throws them out. After he's gone through a dozen, he complains bitterly that people steal his pencils!"

Then there was Harold Ross, over in drama—with a mania
about germs. He spent fifteen minutes every morning, painstakingly washing the top of his desk. Greg Watson on the city
desk had the reporters crazy. "He's pencil happy—can't resist
the urge to change a reporter's copy. If the reporter writes
said, he changes it to *replied*—or vice versa!"

David listened to this gossip wistfully. "I wonder if I'll ever
be a part of it," he told Alice. "Sometimes I feel so far re-

moved I might as well be in Siberia!"

"Don't worry," she replied. "You won't be spending the rest of your life in the shack. It might be sooner than you think."

It was a prophetic remark.

The two finished dinner and attended a foreign movie in a nearby theater. Then they went up to Alice's house, where David was welcomed with warmth and friendliness.

Alice told her parents about David's apartment and her father immediately volunteered the use of the car. "You don't think you have much paraphernalia, David, but wait till you start packing!" Mr. Rogers told the young reporter.

The following afternoon, as David took a final look around at the small room where he had lived since he came to New York, almost two years ago, he remembered this prediction ruefully. "Where in tunket did I acquire all this junk?" he thought. But he would part with none of it—and the notebooks, papers, magazines, books and other paraphernalia all got dumped into the back seat of Mr. Rogers' car. By afternoon, David was comfortably ensconced in his own apartment and hard at work on the arson story.

☆☆☆ *17*

DAVID BECOMES A WRITING REPORTER

THE ARSON ARTICLE was a tough one to write; it didn't have the leavening humor of the two previous ones, and it had to be handled in a different way. It was a challenge, and one David felt he had to meet. He made a list of all the items which

he questioned—dates and places mostly—and then telephoned
Fire Marshal Taylor to have them verified. Since, aside from
the few items that he had jotted down at the start of the interview, he had no written notes other than those he had written
afterwards, this was very necessary to establish accuracy.

When interviewing Taylor, David had done instinctively
what many seasoned reporters learned to do at a later date.
There are always some people who "freeze" at the sight of a
paper and pencil. Somehow the thought that what they are
about to say is going to become public property makes them
cautious—sometimes to the point of silence, other times to
where they will utter only banal inconsequentials. The astute
reporter thereupon puts his paper and pencil away and listens
hard. It's the only thing to do.

David worked on the arson story in his spare time for the
better part of a week. When he finally had it down to his satisfaction, he waited for Thursday, so that he could drop it off
with Holloway when he went to pick up his check.

Once again, he waited at the water cooler for the propitious
moment before approaching the city editor and then walked
forth. Holly spotted him while he was still a distance from the
city desk.

"David! Just the boy I'm looking for!"

David quickened his pace, meanwhile taking the envelope
from his inner jacket pocket. As he reached the city desk, he
placed it before Holly. "This is a little different, Mr. Holloway . . ."

"Another one?" interrupted the city editor, eyebrows raised
in mock surprise. "This is more enterprise than I've seen in a
week of Sundays. Sit down, boy."

To David's dismay, Holly took the copy out of the envelope
and proceeded to read it leisurely. David sat down and watched
him closely, wondering now whether he shouldn't have read
the piece over once more before bringing it in.

Holly's face as he read was a mask. He could have been feeling admiration or contempt—you'd never know which by just watching him. Painfully, David looked away. As his eyes searched the room, he suddenly saw Alice Rogers standing by her desk. She was gazing straight at him and smiling. Briefly she clasped her hands over her head in the manner of a fighter acknowledging applause—and David's spirits rose. He smiled back. "What the heck," he thought. "What am I in a dither about? Either he'll like it or he won't. I did the best I could." Relaxed now, he settled back in his chair.

After a few moments, Holly tossed the last sheet down. "Not bad," he said. "Surprising you got that information out of Taylor—he's such a stick to interview. . . . Further, I think we'll run it tonight. There's a roaring fire going on right now in the huge building that used to house Whitby's department store. We'll use this as a side story."

Holloway removed his glasses, wiped them and continued, "David—I was going to send for you. How would you like to go on general?"

"I sure would," replied David, his heart jumping.

"O.K. You'll start Tuesday. Your days off will be Sunday and Monday, and your hours will be from 11 a.m. to 7 p.m." Holly's gray eyes warmed slightly. "Think you can get used to sleeping nights, for a change?"

"I'd like to try." David laughed.

"Fine!" Holly stood up, putting an end to the interview, and extended his hand. "Good luck, Dave."

"Thanks a million, Mr. Holloway," replied David and walked off on winged feet.

Out at the elevator, Alice was waiting. "What's up?" she asked. "You looked as though you were being electrocuted!"

"Alice—I'm going on general! Beginning Tuesday!"

Alice beamed up at him. "Exit David the leg man. Enter David the general reporter. You'll be a good one, too." She kissed him quickly on the cheek and was gone before he realized what had happened. Grinning foolishly, he left the building.

David could hardly wait to tell Bill Baxter. The veteran reporter clapped him heartily on the shoulder, saying, "You'll do all right, Dave—don't worry about it. Within a few years, you'll probably be one of the best reporters in the city." He smiled thoughtfully. "You've got curiosity and integrity—and you can write. The difficulty with most reporters in town is that they aren't half as good as they think they are. You're a refreshing opposite."

Working in the city room again was at once familiar and strange to David. His nine months as a copy boy had given him a solid grounding in the workings of a newspaper, and his thirteen months on the district had given him some practical working experience. He was now ready to sink or swim.

The problem was theoretical at the moment, however. Since David was a new man, he wasn't given much at first. He was an unknown potential and, since there were plenty of reporters around, the natural tendency was to give assignments to the experienced men.

But there was a bright side to this, too. For one thing, he was now in the same office with Alice—and he could see her there four days a week, since she was off Saturday and Sunday.

They often worked it so that they had lunch at the same time. In bad weather, they would eat in the *Ledger* cafeteria. Other times they would go to a restaurant a short distance from the office. And when things were dull for both of them, there was always the telephone. Fortunately, they could dial each other direct, and by-pass the ubiquitous Suzy.

David was also fortunate in that he was given a desk right next to Courtenay (Red) Platt, a Pulitzer Prize winner. Several years ago, Platt had exposed a huge city scandal involving a commissioner of borough works who had parceled out street paving contracts to friends. These friends of the commissioner's had not only overcharged the city, but they had done shoddy work and had kicked back about a million dollars to the commissioner. While it was basically a local story, it was carried throughout New York and adjoining states, which, just to be on the safe side, conducted investigations of their own.

As a result of Platt's series of articles, which had led to the appointment of a special investigator to look into the charges —all of which Platt had documented before he even touched his typewriter—the city had put in stringent regulations which made it impossible for such skullduggery ever to happen again.

"I remember you," Platt said when David took over the desk next to him. "You're the boy who beat the town on Scott Avery in that plane crash."

"That was over a year ago," David said. "I'd almost forgotten it. I assumed everybody else had, too. Nice of you to remember."

"I never forget anything," Platt said in mock seriousness, then added earnestly, "I remember the first day I came into this office, twelve years ago, and saw Holloway. He looked as tough as he was big. I sure had him all wrong. He put me on the district at first, too. Wonderful experience. But no point in telling you. You're just off it."

At that moment, Fred Blankenship, the assistant day city editor, walked over to David and said, "I'm switching an obituary over to your extension, David. Probably worth a couple of paragraphs. It's from an undertaker. The family gave him all the facts."

The undertaker was an old hand at phoning in obits. David found that the man had all the basic material and all he had to do—just like a rewrite man—was to put the facts together, in *Ledger* style, with the age going immediately after the deceased's name.

This was going to be David's first piece of copy written in the office and he wanted to make it letter-perfect. Ten minutes after he handed his copy in, a copy boy came to his desk and said, "Mr. Holloway would like to see you." David almost tripped in his haste to get to the city desk.

"David," Holloway said in a deceptively avuncular tone, "the obit page is one of the best read in any newspaper. That's why it is so important that every obit be just right. You can be sure that, in addition to the public at large, relatives of the deceased are going to read it closely."

"Yes sir," David said. "I can appreciate that."

"Well," Holloway continued, "you say in your copy that this man died of 'heart failure.' "

"That's right," David said. "That's what the undertaker told me."

"Did he say 'heart failure' or did he say 'heart attack'?"

"Er—now that you mention it, Mr. Holloway, I'm not sure."

"David," the city editor said, not too unkindly, "you made the same error that hundreds of other writing beginners have made on newspapers. Everybody dies of heart failure—including the soldier fatally wounded in the head in combat in war, the child run over by a truck, the woman suffering from a malignancy discovered too late. We all die when our heart fails. But what caused the heart to fail? That's important."

David returned to his desk, crestfallen. He was annoyed with himself. Platt noticed that he was upset and asked him what was wrong. David told him.

Platt smiled and said, "You know, a few years from now you'll look back at this incident and laugh. Not that you'll ever forget it. You never forget any dealings with Holloway. Something similar happened to me when I first started writing my own stuff."

"What was that?" David asked, already beginning to feel better. Here was a Pultizer Prize winner confessing that he had made mistakes, too.

"I covered a luncheon one day," Platt began. "It was at the Ivy League Club. One of the speakers was the *Ledger's* top man in person—the famous Everett Lloyd Banks. As you know, there has been one Banks or another running this newspaper for more than fifty years. I was extremely careful to quote our Mr. Banks most accurately and, when my story was finished, I was, as I recall, quite pleased with myself. The copy was triple-spaced and quite clean. I made sure it was clean because I typed it over and over again to be positive there were no typos or erasures."

There was a gleam in Platt's gray eyes as he continued. "Boy, did I almost go through the floor a few minutes later. Holly sent a copy boy over for me to report to the city desk— just as he did a moment ago with you. He must have mellowed since then, though, because he wasn't quite as pleasant with me as he seems to have been with you."

"What happened?" David cut in.

" 'Courtenay,' he said to me—a name I've always detested, by the way—'I'm glad to see that you've given Everett Lloyd Banks his full name—and not used just the initial L for his middle name. Mr. Banks is proud of his full name and likes to see it all in print.

" 'However,' and at this point his voice was clearly heard by every person in the city room, 'he also likes to think that people around here—at his own newspaper—know just who he is. You refer to him in your copy as publisher of the *Ledger*. He isn't the publisher. He is the editor. Think you can remember that?' "

"I guess you've not only remembered that—but remembered it well," David said.

Platt ran his long, lean fingers through his mop of brick-red hair and exclaimed, "You know, when Everett Lloyd Banks called me up to his office after I won that Pulitzer Prize I told him about that incident. I hesitated, but I did it anyway. I figured he wouldn't fire me, you know, not with that award. He roared."

David found himself assigned to the same things he had been covering on the district—stories involving police and firemen. But now he not only covered them, he also wrote them, coming back to the office to do so.

Minor changes were made in his copy, but basically it appeared in print the way he wrote it. Often, when time permitted, he would show his copy to Alice before he handed it in to the city desk and sometimes she would make a suggestion.

Once he wrote a story about an aspiring young actress who had attempted suicide because of her failure to make any headway in the theater. He described her as having "henna" hair.

"Oh, no!" Alice protested. "The reader—especially the women readers of that story—will know right away that her hair coloring was artificial if you call it 'henna.' Wouldn't you get the same effect if you call her hair 'auburn'?"

"Never thought of it that way," David said, smiling. He thereupon crossed out "henna" and changed it to "auburn."

"That's a more delicate—and kinder—description," Alice said.

While David was doing crime stories, he was not getting the top ones. They were going to people like Red Platt, who continually amazed David with the background information on various racketeers and police officials that he had in his head. And these racketeers and officials knew him, too.

"One of the strangest I've ever dealt with is Fred Carstairs," Platt told David. "You know, he's the former bootlegger, now in trouble on income tax evasion charges.

"Believe it or not, his aim is to achieve respectability—be invited and accepted by the so-called 'good' people. He's got all the money he'll ever need, but he's been in gambling and various other underworld activities all his life, so that it's impossible for him to get out of these rackets. He also owns considerable real estate—but the government has tied up all those assets with liens until it disposes of the income tax case against him."

"What's he really like?" David asked. "I get the impression from some of the newspapers in town that he's a ruthless man, one who would not stop at murder to put through a deal. Is that right?"

"Well, that may have been true years ago, though I'm sure he could never be convicted for such a crime—assuming he ever committed murder. Strong arm stuff, yes—but murder, I don't think so. As you know, he's been called in for questioning on many homicides and other crimes, but the only time he was ever convicted was when he was about twenty years old —and that was thirty-five years ago. And what was the charge? Stealing a neighbor's car. For that, he got two years in state prison.

"He doesn't care at all when he sees himself referred to in print as an often-suspected murderer, former rum runner, racketeer, big-time gambler or what have you. But the thing that drives him mad is when he picks up a newspaper and reads, *ex-convict* Fred Carstairs."

"Well, he is an ex-convict, isn't he?" David inquired.

"Of course, he is—but he takes the view that he went to jail for a crime he committed before most of the current batch of reporters were in kindergarten. I know I can always get a

rise out of him by so referring to him. Though one day he
called me up at home after he had seen a story I had written
for the *Ledger* and demanded, 'How'd you find that out?'

" 'What are you referring to?'

" 'You know—where you call me a former fish peddler.'

" 'Oh that—I learned it from one of your so-called
cronies.'

" 'Well, I'd rather be called an ex-fish peddler than an ex-
convict.' "

"By the way," David said, "I noticed that you said that Carstairs called you at home. Where did he get your number? Is it
in the phone book?"

"It wasn't then—since it was an unlisted number. I had
given it to him. While I, of course, never went out socially
with him, I used to run into him around town and, just as I
made it a habit to exchange telephone numbers with police
and other officials, I thought it would be a good idea to do it
with this racketeer, too. Never know when he might want to
call me, or I him. You see, he learned to trust me, and I may
have been the only reporter in town who had his unlisted number. It paid off, too."

"How so?" David wanted to know.

"Well, you may recall—no, this was before you came to
the *Ledger*—when 'Two-Gun' Mike Mandolin, a long-time
enemy of Fred Carstairs, was beaten up in the men's room of
a night club. Mandolin told the cops that Fred Carstairs was
behind the assault—that while Carstairs, of course, didn't
administer the beating, personally, a couple of his goons carried out the assignment for him."

"Was Carstairs behind it?" David wanted to know.

"I'm getting to that. Let me tell this my own way."

David smiled sheepishly as Platt continued. "Immediately,
police issued a thirteen-state alarm for Carstairs. As you prob-

ably know, every time the New York City police issues an alarm for someone, it goes on a thirteen-state police network. After a while the alarm spreads to all forty-eight states.

"Sometimes cops—like reporters—forget basics. You'd think that they would have hit his home, or at least one of the hotels he is regularly seen at. Every day for years he has been going to the same swank barber shop for a shave and shoe shine, after which he goes to a hotel, where he spends an hour or so taking steam baths, polishing it off with a brief swim in the hotel's pool.

"I took it for granted that the cops had checked out those places, as well as his home, for after two days he was still listed among the missing—and wanted. At least it figured they would keep detectives posted at those spots.

"I don't know what impelled me, but, since I had his home number, I thought I'd give it a try. I figured the worst that could happen was that I would get no answer or, if I did, and the phone was picked up by his butler, he would give me the brush-off.

"Well, believe it or not, David, Fred Carstairs—the one and only—answered the phone.

" 'What's up?' he asked me.

" 'You kidding?' I said. 'The cops have been looking for you—and you ask me what's up.'

" 'I've been out on my yacht and haven't heard or seen any news report for the last week.'

"Well, to make this longish story short, I told him about how 'Two-Gun' Mike Mandolin had been beaten up and that he was wanted as the mastermind of the assault. Carstairs said what I expected him to say—ridiculous."

"Is that the end of the anecdote?" David asked.

"Almost—but not quite. I arranged with Carstairs to surrender at Police Headquarters the following evening—and I alerted the picture editor, so that the *Ledger* was the only paper in town to get a shot of Carstairs walking into headquarters. Needless to say, while he was booked—on the complaint of Mandolin—he was soon turned loose. There just was no case against him—only Mandolin's word."

David wondered how long it would be before he might be on an exchange telephone number basis with people in the public's eye—notorious or otherwise. Platt had a loose leaf notebook which he kept in his desk drawer and it contained the private number of practically anybody of news value—on city, state and federal levels. But it had taken him years to collect these, having covered every conceivable kind of story, though his first love was still crime. "If I were to lose this notebook, I'd be like a man with one arm," said Platt.

Then he picked up a little green book, with an imitation leather cover, to check the spelling of a recently appointed judge. It was an odd spelling—Bishopp, with two ps.

"This, by the way," Platt told David, holding the little green book in his left hand, "is invaluable. It's put out by the city and it lists the judges of every court, the names of every city and state commissioner and their deputies, as well as other key personnel, and hundreds of other such vital bits of information that a reporter must have at one time or another. Not only that, but it gives their office telephone numbers and their home addresses."

"Where can I get one?"

"Ask Holloway's secretary if she has an extra one kicking around. The city puts out a limited number and sells them for a nominal price—something like a dollar. They come out once a year. It's extremely rare that you'll find an error in it. It's considered the backlog of the newspaper business. If Holloway's secretary hasn't any more, you can use mine—I keep it in the same drawer with my loose leaf notebook."

★★★ *18*

HIS FIRST STORIES

DAVID BEGAN TO MAKE it a practice to keep his own list of telephone numbers. He also bought a loose leaf notebook—the kind that would fit into an outside jacket pocket. One of the first names he put into it was that of George Wright, the president of a catch-all union, which had among its members laborers as well as white collar workers.

David had never covered any labor story, so when the city desk sent him out one day to cover an impending strike at one of the largest concerns in town, he didn't know just what to do. He turned to Red Platt.

"Get both sides—that's rule number 1," Platt advised him. "You'll probably find that the company will say that the union is asking for the moon, while the union will say that the company is paying a below living wage.

"Get the union's exact demands—and exactly what the company is offering. And try to give statements from both sides. Labor can be a ticklish thing to handle—and it has become more and more newsworthy in recent years. Handle it exactly like a police story. Don't make any observations on your own. The *Ledger* is neutral in its news columns. Our editorial page may be for one side in the controversy, but you be sure to be impartial."

David did just that and, after he mentioned the impending strike at the company, he gave the issues, the demands, the offers and brief statements from both sides. It was, David

had to admit, a not too exciting story at this stage of the
game, though he could see that, if the strike did come off,
throwing thousands of people out of work, it would make page
one for sure.

David got a phone call from Wright the day his story appeared in the *Ledger*.

"Young man," Wright said to him, "I want to thank you
for giving us a square deal in this morning's *Ledger*. It presented the issues fairly—as compared to some of the other
papers. But then the *Ledger* has always been fair. If you need
any further information on the situation, don't hesitate to call
me—any time, even at my home."

That was how David got his first unlisted number on his
own. As it turned out, he had no immediate use for it, since
mediators had been called in and the impending strike was settled.

At times, it seemed, crime took a holiday. Of course, there
was always a certain amount of holdups and assaults, but
often they were of the one-paragraph variety and could be
cleaned up in short order.

It was the middle of a hot summer, on a Thursday, when
Holloway called David over to the city desk, shortly after he
came in at 11 a.m., and said, "Kind of quiet today. However,
this might make a story. We've gotten several phone calls from
women who say that, for the last several days, they have been
bothered by aphids and have been unable to sit in the west
side park—you know, the one at the river. Go up there and
see what you can find out."

David took the subway up to the park, which covered fifty
acres. There were scores of women sitting on the park benches
and numerous maids with toddlers. David looked for aphids—
those little green insects. He saw none, but he thought he
couldn't very well go back to the office and say, "No aphids,

Mr. Holloway."

Just who had called the *Ledger* he did not know. The callers had left neither their names nor addresses.

David walked up to a middle-aged woman sitting alone on a bench.

"Excuse me, madam, but have you been bothered by aphids?" David asked. The woman jumped up from the bench and, glaring at him, snapped, "Young man, don't try to flirt with me! Get somebody closer to your own age. This park is becoming impossible for a respectable woman."

David thought of running after her and explaining his position. But he feared, if he pursued her, she might panic and scream. It gave him an uncomfortable feeling—did he look like a thug?

David walked up to a young woman in white, taking care of a toddler who was crawling on the grass.

No sooner did he open his mouth and say, "Excuse me"— than the young woman took the child in her arms and left the park.

When his next two attempts met with similar rebuffs, David said to himself, "Oh, my gosh! These people don't know who I am! I seem to have forgotten what almost cost me my life —forgetting to wear my press card!"

He immediately attached his press card to his jacket lapel, since, because of the heat, he was hatless. At first, several women thought he was some kind of salesman, but when he got up closer and they saw the red card emblazoned "Press," they were willing to talk to him—and at great length. In fact, some of them asked, "Aren't you going to take my picture?"

It developed that the area was indeed plagued with aphids, and David returned to the *Ledger* and wrote a story, quoting these women by name. Their common lament was—though there appeared to be no aphids that particular day—that the park was becoming uninhabitable because of the aphids.

While the story was put on an inside page of the *Ledger*, in an inconspicuous spot, enough city officials read it to cause the area to be sprayed with an insecticide. That, of course, made for a follow-up story for the *Ledger*.

One month later—when David had completely forgotten the aphid story—he was in a police station, getting the details on a robbery.

After he had gathered all the information and was about to leave the detective squad room, a rather short man, a total stranger to David, said to him: "Still chasing aphids?"

"I beg your pardon?"

"You still chasing aphids?"

"I don't get it," David said.

The stranger laughed and pulled a shield out of his pocket.

"I'm detective Alfred King. About a month ago, I was on the park detail. I spotted you going up to lone women. I figured, at first, that you were up to no good. I saw those women run away from you. But I couldn't pull you in unless I had a witness, a complainant to charge you with something like disorderly conduct.

"Then I saw you pull out what appeared to be a press card. But I wasn't taking any chances. I spoke to several of the women—those who didn't run away, I mean—after you did. They told me what you were after.

"I sized you up pretty good, even though you never noticed me. I figured you were legitimate—and harmless. I stopped tailing you after a while. And I saw the story in the *Ledger* the next morning. Not a bad story."

David was pleased at the last statement but not a little uneasy to realize he had been under such close scrutiny—and completely unaware of it!

He couldn't wait to pass that incident on to Alice. She laughed aloud. "Imagine him regarding you as a menace!"

"It's a real queer feeling to learn you've been followed," David told her. "And those ladies!" he recalled. "First I couldn't get them to talk, and then I couldn't get them to stop!"

"That's why they call us an 'unpredictable' sex," Alice replied. "Incidentally," she continued, "do you want to go to an opening tonight?"

When a new play opened in town, there were occasionally an extra pair of tickets, when someone in drama couldn't make it. The drama desk then—very cautiously—offered the tickets to friends at the paper. They kept this very quiet, for fear of being inundated with requests for future tickets.

But Alice and David, who had attended a few openings before, had learned to their sorrow that, when the drama desk offered tickets, more often than not the play was very poor. Most shows had out-of-town openings, and bad reports flooded the town well in advance of the unfortunate play.

An opening, however, was still a gala occasion, where the theatergoers dressed formally and there was an air of excitement about the whole evening.

"Sure," replied David. "At least we'll have good seats."

They did have good seats—row E on the aisle. And the play was mildly amusing—but no more. However, they enjoyed being together.

☆☆☆ *19*

DAVID'S REPUTATION IS AT STAKE

AS DAVID EFFICIENTLY HANDLED the more routine stories in the city room, the city desk's confidence in him grew. They started sending him out on the more important stories as they happened.

The one thing every reporter dreads is a letter of complaint —wherein some person who figures in a news story complains either that he was "misquoted" by a reporter or that the reporter did not write the true facts.

Where a public record exists, or where the person who claims he was "misquoted" was overheard to say the same thing by a number of other people, he is obviously, of course, trying to squirm out of an embarrassing situation. But it can frequently happen that interviewer and interviewee offer different versions of a private tête-à-tête. There are no witnesses, and the interviewee claims that the published report is untruthful. In a situation of this sort, the reporter has only his reputation to fall back on. If he is known to be methodical and accurate, his city desk will back him up. If, on the other hand, he has made careless errors in the past, his position is in serious jeopardy—for he can place his newspaper in a dangerous position: as untrustworthy and unreliable and also as the defendant in a libel action.

Even should the newspaper print a retraction of a false statement, this has little effect either morally or legally, for it is an old axiom that "everybody sees the charges, but nobody reads the retractions."

A reporter, therefore, is in a position of immense trust, and David was fully aware of his responsibilities. He took copious notes and evolved his own system of shorthand and abbreviations.

Where the real, old-time reporters still took notes on copy paper, generally folded three ways—giving them three "sides" —the newer crop, including David, leaned toward cardboard-covered notebooks, with lined pages. These books fitted comfortably into a jacket pocket, and they had one big advantage over copy paper—the pages did not scatter, and the entire book could be kept for future reference a lot more easily than a mass of copy paper.

Instead of writing out the word "the," David wrote just a dot. Instead of writing the words "for" or "four," he put down the numeral 4. Similarly, for "to," "too" or "two," he wrote the numeral 2. Those were some of the short cuts he developed in taking notes. Also, he found he could make other abbreviations and read them back after a while without too much difficulty. Certainly the letter "u" meant "you."

The word "would" became "wd," "learn" became "ln," "talk" became "tk," "defendant" became "def.," "prosecutor" became "pros.," "judge" became just "J." It was not quite shorthand, but it helped him immeasurably. Certainly, if anybody else tried to read David's notes, he would have trouble. But David had heard that even those who had studied the recognized shorthand methods made their own additional short forms which nobody else could understand either.

David had his private shorthand system well under way when Hartford Ames, a well-known business man, was brought into Traffic Court as a chronic traffic violator. In the previous two years, he had piled up twenty-five tickets—and had ignored every one of them.

The drive against such violators was being conducted by one judge of the court, before whom Ames was brought.

Ames pleaded guilty to all but one of the tickets. He admitted to having either parked illegally or parking overtime in restricted areas a total of twenty-four times.

But on the ticket charging him with speeding, he pleaded innocent—and asked for a lengthy delay before trial. Ames knew that, if he were found guilty on this speeding charge, it would mean automatic loss of his driver's license, having twice been convicted on the same charge before. The illegal parking tickets had no bearing on a person's losing his license, since the city took the view that, if it revoked licenses on those grounds, a good percentage of the drivers would have to give up their cars.

"I see no reason for a delay on the speeding charge," Judge Gerald Morton intoned severely. "You have pleaded guilty on the other charges after two years and I see no reason why you should get a delay on the twenty-fifth ticket. You're probably guilty on that as well."

While David's experience in courts was limited, he'd had enough to know that this was a most improper comment for a judge to make in open court—for the record. David had no trouble writing down the exact words that Judge Morton had said, since he was a slow speaker—and besides, David had worked his short forms up to the point where he was almost able to write as fast as a shorthand stenographer.

Mr. Ames, a layman, obviously did not realize the impropriety of the judge's remark that he was "probably guilty." The lawyer who was with him either did not hear it or, for reasons best known to himself, did not object.

However, there was a short trial delay granted—for one day.

The next day, Mr. Ames showed up with a different lawyer, who opened the proceedings by saying that he had just been retained and that he had two motions to make.

The first was that he would like to have at least a two-week delay before start of the trial so that he could familiarize himself with the facts in the case and prepare a proper defense.

The second motion was to have Judge Morton disqualify himself from presiding in the case.

"On what grounds do you want me to disqualify myself?" Judge Morton demanded, his neck turning red with anger.

"On grounds of prejudice, Your Honor."

"Prejudice? What prejudice? Do you have any evidence to that effect?"

"Yes, Your Honor, I do."

"What is it—show me the evidence!"

"In this morning's *Ledger*—the account dealing with my

client's appearance in this court yesterday."

"Newspaper reports are not evidence, Counselor. But since this is only a motion you're making, proceed."

The lawyer thereupon read David's account, which quoted the judge as having said: "You're probably guilty on that (speeding charge) as well."

"I never said that!" the judge thundered. "I was misquoted."

David, who had been standing near the bench, went white with anger. By denying his account in the *Ledger*, the judge was in effect terming it a fictitious story and the author of it was thereupon held up to the courtroom as irresponsible and unreliable.

David was dead certain that the quote was completely accurate, but decorum prohibited him from saying anything. Fuming, he kept quiet and bided his time.

The court proceeding ended a few minutes later. The judge refused to disqualify himself, maintaining he was not prejudiced, though he did grant a one-week trial postponement on the speeding charge.

No sooner did the judge leave the bench, than David looked at his book for the notes of the day before. They showed that the judge had used just those words. But David knew that this was by no means conclusive evidence. He sought out the court stenographer.

Whatever was in that stenographer's notes was what counted. That was the official record. David had heard of rare instances—though he had no firsthand knowledge—where judges had doctored their own remarks with the court stenographer.

That's why, David felt, it was important that he get hold of the stenographer before the judge did—assuming the judge had a mind to fool around with the record.

It developed that the stenographer recording the judge's

denial of prejudice was not the same one who had sat the day before—and would have those vital words. The stenographer that David wanted was nowhere in the building. He had left for home. David went to the chief stenographer's office and got the home phone number of the stenographer he wanted.

He called him up.

"What do you want this information for?" the stenographer asked cagily.

"Oh, I just want to check something the judge said yesterday, that's all. Something about the speeding charge involving Ames."

"Well, I haven't transcribed my notes on the typewriter yet."

"Do you have your notes at home with you?"

"Yes."

"Well, all I want is just that one bit—just what did the judge say?"

The stenographer read from his notes: "You're probably guilty on that as well."

"Thank you very much," David said.

That was all he needed.

David rushed back to the *Ledger* office. He couldn't wait to tell Holloway about this—and how the *Ledger* had been, in effect, slandered.

David poured out the details to Holloway and the more he related, the angrier Holloway got.

"Call that judge up," Holloway snapped. "Tell him that you've checked the official record. Ask him what he's going to do about it."

David called up the judge.

"How did you check the record?" Judge Morton asked David. "I haven't seen it myself."

"I called the stenographer at his home. He read it to me."

"Oh," the judge said. "Well, you know it could be that the stenographer didn't hear me correctly. I don't recall saying that—not in those words, anyway."

Here, David felt, the judge must have known he used those very words—and was lying in his teeth.

"Oh, I don't think this is anything to get excited about," the judge continued airily. "Even if I did use those words, it was just one of those things, that's all. Why not forget it."

"Sir," David said, "you made me—and worse than that, the *Ledger,* sound irresponsible in court."

"Oh, forget it, it was just one of those things," the judge repeated.

Then the judge hung up.

David passed this along to Holloway.

"What?" Holloway snorted. "He's not going to get away with that!"

Holloway picked up a phone. "Suzy, get me Judge Morton. And I want him—no secretary or anything like that. Hurry it up."

Within thirty seconds, Judge Morton was on the other end of the phone.

"Judge, this is Holloway, city editor of the *Ledger.*"

"Oh, hello, Mr. Holloway. I've heard some fine things about you. What can I do for you?"

The judge was acting as if nothing had happened and as if David had not even registered a complaint.

"Look, Judge, you know darn well what I'm calling about. Our man White quotes you as saying that this was just one of those things—and for us to forget it."

"Well—er, Mr. Holloway, what can I do? As I said, it was an unfortunate thing, and I'm sorry it happened."

"I'll tell you what you're going to do, Judge!" Holly's tone was acid and biting. "You're going to apologize to the *Ledger* in open court! When this case comes up before you again, a week from today, you're going to set the record straight. You're going to state that the *Ledger* account as written by White was accurate. It's no concern of mine whether you disqualify yourself or not—but the *Ledger* is a reliable and a responsible newspaper, and we value our reputation!"

The judge knew that he could not afford to antagonize a man like Holly and a paper like the *Ledger*.

"I'll work it out," the judge promised.

"And White will be in court to see that you do," Holloway said, banging the receiver down to end the conversation.

Sure enough, when the case came up the following week, the judge, in his own stilted way, put into the record that he was sorry about what he said in regard to the *Ledger's* account and concluded that the *Ledger* did in fact quote him accurately.

And to cap the matter, Judge Morton disqualified himself from the case.

☆☆☆ *20*

HIS FIRST BONUS

MORE AND MORE, David was being assigned to cases of crime, and he couldn't have been happier. A good crime story was not too hard to handle—and he never understood why some of the veteran reporters shied away from them. "Too much work," they complained. Also, there was a tremendous amount of responsibility. A crime story was avidly read by all readers—and a reporter who neglected to call back a particular detective, or was too lazy to leave the office and got all his information by phone, or did not make the extra effort to track down somebody who could shed additional light on a particular phase of the story—found his printed account was a bad second, or even third, when compared with those in the other newspapers. And as if his own embarrassment were not enough, he was sure to catch it from Holloway—in full hearing of the entire city room!

The fear of failure did not deter David—primarily because he was not lazy, and he was of an inquisitive nature. He not only wanted to be in possession of all the facts for his story— he wanted to know them for himself. He liked all the parts of a puzzle to fit together.

It happened that David handled a story involving the arrest of a hotel jewel thief. The detective who made the pinch was none other than Terry Mulligan, and when they met in the squad room, they fell on each other like long-lost brothers.

The thief, Mulligan explained, was a smooth operator. He would check into one of the city's better hotels under an assumed name and with practically no luggage. After he had been there a while, he would spend considerable time chatting with the room clerk.

Being glib and gregarious, the thief was able to carry on a conversation on a number of subjects. He was especially up on sports. As he would converse with the room clerk, other persons registered at the same hotel would drop their room keys before going out for the evening.

The thief, Mulligan continued, would "palm" one key at a time—right under the nose and without the knowledge of the room clerk.

"When he had about four keys—of persons he knew were well to do—the thief would tell the room clerk that he had some phone calls to make and walk away," Mulligan said. "Then he would pick up a house phone and call the room of the person who he figured would have the largest amount of valuables. Naturally, since that person had just walked out of the hotel, the thief would get no answer from the room. He would then take the elevator up, walk to that room and knock on the door—just to make sure. If he got no answer to that knock, in he would go—and help himself. Shortly thereafter, he would bid the room clerk a fond good-bye and check out— always paying his bill, of course."

On the basis of this information from Mulligan, David wrote the story. The other newspapers had pretty much the same account, since the American Press had also gotten the facts.

But, while David printed the story, he expressed some private reservations to Mulligan the following day.

"You can't tell me that a man could stand and talk to a room clerk and steal big hotel keys right out from under the man's nose!" sniffed David. "That thief got in those rooms some other way!"

"You want to see me do it?" asked Mulligan.

"What do you mean?"

"Meet me outside the Lord Ransom Hotel at six this evening."

David kept the date. This, he knew, was the same hotel from which that thief had been "palming" the room keys and then making off with considerable loot.

"You just sit yourself in that chair over there," Mulligan told David, "and watch me. Keep your head buried in a newspaper. Whatever you do, don't let on in any way that you know me."

David did just that.

He saw Mulligan—who also had a gift of gab—go over to the room clerk and act as if he were a regular patron of the hotel. Before long, the clerk was laughing at some tale that Mulligan related. Of course, as they were together, keys were being dropped at the clerk's desk. David saw Mulligan pick up a total of six in less than twenty minutes—and pocket them. When Mulligan walked away from the desk, the clerk was still laughing.

Mulligan then went through the same routine as the real thief—up to a point. He telephoned the rooms, established that nobody was in at the moment, went up, knocked on the door, got no response—and stopped there.

Then Mulligan returned to the lobby with the six keys and sought out the hotel detective—or more specifically, the private detective in charge of the hotel's security.

"You might be interested in these," Mulligan said to the private detective. "I picked them up while talking to one of your room clerks. I could have hit each one of those rooms and emptied them of all their valuables."

David rushed back to the *Ledger* and told Holloway what he had just witnessed.

"O.K., let's get it written," Holloway said. "But to protect your friend Mulligan, it might be a good idea to leave his name out of the story. As it is, the other papers will suspect that you were invited to go along on this and watch Mulligan operate. They'll find out soon enough who the detective was. But let's make it tough for them."

David wrote the story—exactly as he had seen and heard it.

The *Ledger* put it on page one—with David's byline. Though he referred to the fact that a reporter witnessed the detective's operations, David never used the words "this reporter" or "I." He disliked personal horn-blowing.

Within an hour after the first edition of the *Ledger* came out on the street, the manager of the Lord Ransom called up the newspaper. He was bitter. He insisted on speaking to the managing editor—who was not around. He asked for "this person David White," but he had already left for the evening, having a dinner date with Alice. The hotel manager finally wound up with Holloway.

"That story you have in the *Ledger* is libelous—and unless you take it out of your next edition and print a full retraction in the same space on page 1, we are going to sue!" the hotel manager thundered ominously.

"I'm sorry, sir," Holloway said. "But we know the story is true. It will stay in the paper—just where it is on page 1."

"Not only will we sue, but we'll also cancel our advertisements out of the *Ledger!*" the manager threatened.

"That, sir, is entirely up to you."

David's story created a sensation. The other morning newspapers were unable to check it out in time, but the afternoon papers were able to establish its authenticity the next day— and they played it up big, too, with basically the same story that David had written.

The upshot was that the Lord Ransom Hotel—as well as all the better hotels in town—thereupon established chutes, in which patrons were told to drop their keys. Also, the Lord Ransom never filed any libel suit—nor did it stop advertising in the *Ledger*. Moreover, Mulligan did not get into trouble with his superiors for letting a reporter watch him work.

"I guess your friendship with Mulligan paid off," Holloway said to David. "If you'll look at the bulletin board, you'll also see a more material payoff."

There David found a neatly-typed note:

David White gets a $25 bonus for his exclusive story on the hotel. E. E. H.

CRIMINAL COURTS

A FEW MONTHS LATER, David found himself assigned to the courts.

His new assignment came about as a result of Holloway's feeling that a young reporter should get some grounding in as many different types of stories as possible. Besides, it was a natural for David to cover courts. He had been doing mostly police stories, with a smattering of parades, luncheons, ship news, labor and even religion.

Jerry Savage, who had been covering the Criminal Courts Building, was coming into the office to work on rewrite, and Holly deputized David to the vacated court beat. However, Holloway made it clear that, from time to time, he would also be called upon to do general assignments.

The pressroom in the Criminal Courts Building—a huge, eighteen-story structure which also housed the city prison in a separate wing—was on the street floor, just off the center of the block-long lobby. This pressroom was a far cry from the one used by the east side district reporters. It not only was air-conditioned, but it also had a television set. In fact, it really was two large rooms, separated by doors which were infrequently closed. The rear room, the larger of the two, had six telephone booths.

Though there was a circular information desk—twenty feet in diameter—in the center of the lobby, it often was unmanned. Consequently, the almost—but not quite—invisible sign saying "Press" brought all kinds of people into that room.

"Where is the Probation Department?"

"Where is the Juvenile Aid Society?"

"Where is the Legal Aid Society?"

"Where is Traffic Court?"

"Where is the District Attorney's office?"

Where indeed, were all those places?

A whole new world opened up for David in the Criminal Courts Building.

There he was to see the same people he had seen in police stations when they were first arrested. Now they were to be tried on various charges—peddling dope, burglary, embezzling, speeding, murder.

"Basically," Platt explained to David when he learned of his new assignment, "there are two principal criminal trial courts. One is known as Special Sessions, where misdemeanor, or lesser crimes, are tried. They are punishable upon conviction by a maximum of one year in jail or an indeterminate sentence up to three years. This court is presided over by three judges—so that there can be a split decision."

"So far I follow you," David said.

"Good! The more serious charges—or felonies—are tried in General Sessions, also known as County Court. Here the punishment could be up to life imprisonment, or even death, for cases involving first-degree murder. In this court, there is only one judge presiding, but he does not decide whether a defendant is innocent or guilty.

"That is strictly the function of the jury, which, as you know, consists of twelve persons. And in contrast to Special Sessions—where there is no jury—the verdict has to be unanimous. If a jury stands at eleven to one for conviction—and that twelfth juror refuses to budge from his position—then it is considered a 'hung' or 'deadlocked' jury and no verdict is returned. The defendant is subject to trial on the same charge all over again—before another jury."

"Isn't that double jeopardy?" David asked Platt.

"No, it is not. That jury did not come in with any decision—so it is as if there had been no trial at all. Similarly, there have been cases where a trial has lasted for five weeks and was declared a mistrial by the judge without even submitting the case to the jury. A mistrial is also like no trial—meaning that it must start all over again, before a new jury."

Platt was obviously enjoying relating these basic facts—and David was listening closely.

"The most dramatic trials are generally those for first-degree murder," Platt went on. "Incidentally, every conviction in this state for first-degree murder must be reviewed on appeal by the state's highest court—the Court of Appeals. It doesn't matter whether the defendant is penniless; that court must review such a conviction. The state, you see, is in no hurry to put a convicted murderer to death without giving him every chance to escape the electric chair."

Alice Rogers, over in the Sunday section, was at that moment thinking of dialing David. She looked toward his desk, to see if he were free. He seemed to be too engrossed. He was, indeed, for he was asking Platt, "How many times can a person be tried for the same thing?"

"Believe it or not," Platt replied, "there was one man who stood trial for first-degree murder six times. Yes, I said *six*. I think he holds the record in this state."

"Never heard of it—what was his name?"

"Mike Felix. Mike was in the shadow of the electric chair for eight years. He was a sharp-faced, undersized thug and he was appropriately named 'Death House Mike.' In the more than two years that he was actually quartered near the hot seat, he saw thirty-five other murderers walk the last mile."

"Is this fiction or fact?"

"Fact, boy. Anyway, his luck finally ran out and he was strapped in the chair and burned in state prison. At the end, he was all of twenty-seven years old. He was executed almost eight years to the day after he was first convicted for wanton murder."

"Why was he tried *six* times?" David wanted to know.

"Well, Mike and three other young thugs got into serious trouble. They burst into a grocery store and pulled a stick-up. Though the owner offered no resistance, Mike pointed a .38 at the man's heart, fired and killed him instantly.

"Mike's three buddies were picked up almost immediately. Though they did not do the actual slaying, they were in on the crime. Under this state's laws, they were equally culpable. They were convicted and put to death.

"But Mike was not caught until four months after the murder. He was put on trial—the first time—a few days after his wife, who was on relief, gave birth to a daughter, their only child. Mike was convicted and sentenced, like his three confederates, to die in the electric chair."

"I take it there was a postponement," David interjected.

"The Court of Appeals stepped in. It set the verdict aside and ordered a new trial. That court held that 'Death House Mike' had not been allowed to offer evidence at the trial that police wrung a confession out of him during thirty-six hours of questioning.

"He was tried again. This time, the jury was unable to agree on a verdict after deliberating twenty-one hours. It reportedly was nine to three for conviction. He was tried a third time—with the same inconclusive result. On this occasion, it was understood that the jury, out eighteen hours, was ten to two for conviction.

"The district attorney put him on trial a fourth time and

the prosecutor got the verdict he won at the first trial: guilty of murder in the first degree. Mike was thrown back into the Death House.

"But again the Court of Appeals upset the verdict. Now it held that the jury did not receive a proper explanation of why Mike was questioned for thirty-six hours after his arrest before he was arraigned in court."

"Then what happened?"

"I forgot to tell you, David, that the same judge conducted all four trials. He was fed up with Mike. He was certain that, try as the prosecution might, the fellow would never be put to death. The judge then did something that is believed never to have happened before in this state and certainly has never happened since."

"What was that?"

"The judge let Mike go free in bail, fixing the nominal sum of $5,000—this, even though he was still under indictment for the capital crime of first-degree murder.

"For thirty-eight months he roamed the streets—waiting for a fifth trial. He kept himself busy during that period. He pulled other stick-ups, stopping short of murder, however. And on one occasion he beat up a cop.

"But one day he went too far. He stuck up an insurance collector, who didn't mind giving up his money, but pleaded with Mike, 'Please don't take my wrist watch. My wife gave it to me when we were married seven months ago.'

"Mike responded by shooting the collector to death.

"So Mike was now indicted for another first-degree murder. For some strange reason, it was decided not to try him for this new crime, but for the old one, on which he had already stood trial four times—the one involving the murder of the grocery owner.

"The fifth trial for that slaying had hardly got under way

when a police officer who had arrested Mike for that old murder took the stand.

" 'Do you know what happened to your three boy friends?' the officer quoted himself as saying when he arrested Mike for the grocery slaying. 'They were convicted.'

"That did it. The judge—the same one who had conducted the first four trials—held that the words 'They were convicted' were so prejudicial from a legal standpoint, that he had no alternative but to declare a mistrial.

"But Mike was not let out on bail again. He was now put on trial for the murder of the insurance agent.

"There were no disagreements or reversals here. The very first time out, a jury found Mike guilty of first-degree murder. He was sentenced to burn. The Court of Appeals—which had rescued him twice before—saw no reason to interfere this time.

"So on a cold Thursday night 'Death House Mike' began his last walk after a munificent steak dinner.

" 'I am innocent of this!' he cried. 'Why do they do this to me? This is something I never did. I am innocent.' They all say that, you know.

"Three minutes later, he was dead. He had netted a total of sixty-two dollars from his two murders—fifty dollars from the grocer and twelve dollars from the insurance collector. His trials had cost the state at least $50,000.

"And that, David, is the story of the man who stood trial six times for first-degree murder. Go ahead, check the clips. You'll find that I covered all his trials."

David was soon to find out who the so-called "tough" and "soft" judges were, and a myriad of other things. He also learned—with almost dire results—the difference between what is privileged and not privileged.

It happened in Felony Court, where a dope peddler suspect who had been arrested the night before was having a preliminary hearing. The magistrate, because the defendant had previous convictions, held him without bail, pending action of the grand jury. The defendant was represented by counsel, whose lengthy appeal to the judge to have his client released in bail was unsuccessful.

As David walked out of court, he was followed by a swarthy man who identified himself as a brother of the prisoner. The man seemed enraged.

"That judge is nothing but a bum!" he cried. "I know all about him! He's crooked! He only plays ball when you pay him off!"

David got the man's name, address and occupation. He also asked him for more details on his charges.

"You won't print them anyway," the man taunted David.

"Oh, yes I will—you've made them, haven't you?"

Back at his office, David began his story this way:

"The brother of a narcotics suspect peddler charged yesterday that a judge 'only plays ball when you pay him off!' "

David thought that was a pretty snappy lead and showed it to Platt.

Platt whistled.

"What's all this about?" he asked David. "Sounds like you've got a whale of a story."

David explained how the brother followed him outside of court and made his charges.

"Hold it—hold everything!" Platt said. "You can't use that! If that ever got into print, the judge could take over the *Ledger*. Besides, I doubt very much that it's true. I know that judge."

"Why can't I print it?" David was puzzled.

"Because it's not privileged—that's why! Does Holloway know what you're writing?"

"No, he doesn't. What's so terrible?"

"You'd better listen—and listen hard, David. This man

made that statement outside of court. There is no record that he ever said it. Would you print it if he said that the city editor of the *Ledger* beats his reporters? Did you even go up to the judge and ask him if he had any comment on what this man charged? Obviously, you didn't."

"You mean if I got a denial from the judge, then I could print the man's charge and the judge's denial—and then I would be O.K.?"

"No, that's not what I mean at all. You could only print that charge if the man had said it in open court—if it went into the court record, while the court was in session. Anything that's said in open court—remember those two words *open court*—is privileged, meaning you can print whatever is said. Of course, you must also print the denial, if it all goes into the court record, taken down by the court reporter, better known as the court stenographer."

"You mean, then, that anything said outside of court is not privileged?"

"That's exactly what I do mean—and I can't emphasize that too much."

"You mean I can't print anything said outside of court at all?"

"Oh, you can print certain things said outside of court, all right. If the district attorney tells you that his next witness is going to be so and so or the defense counsel tells you that he expects to take three days in which to present his side of the case—that sort of thing is all right. Nothing libelous or damaging about that."

"Well, there goes my snappy lead," David said. "Thanks. Holloway probably would have blown a gasket if I had handed it in."

"And he would have had good reason to, too," Platt told him.

☆☆☆ 22

FRED CARSTAIRS

OCCASIONALLY, David would get a night assignment, to cover an affair at some top hotel or club. This meant a free dinner, of course, but he found after the first few that the principal course was invariably chicken—something he could live without. These fancy shindigs were generally held to aid worthy causes or to honor somebody.

This particular evening, David was assigned to cover a dinner at one of the city's leading hotels. Here a nationally-known and highly respected organization was to announce that it had reached its goal to raise $1,000,000 to aid crippled children of indigent families. It was a $100 a plate affair that would build up a tidy surplus—and most of the city's so-called "best" people were expected to attend.

The organization had sent out a press release—an "advance"—to the *Ledger,* among others. This release mentioned who the principal speakers were to be—and even gave excerpts of their speeches. It also listed the names of various judges and city officials who would be present.

"Give us a short spread on this before you go over to the dinner," Holloway told David, meaning that the reporter should write no more than half a column. "It'll probably come off just as scheduled. You can call in after a while and your story will probably stand all night just as you wrote it—unless, of course, somebody gets shot."

While there was a press table with ten seats, only two reporters showed up—David and Arthur Page, of the *Transcript*. David had met Page on a previous assignment, at which the *Transcript* reporter had not particularly distinguished himself. He had asked not a single question and written an uninspired account.

The grand ballroom of the hotel was being used and there were, as the release had said there would be, about one thousand persons present. All the men wore dinner jackets. (The two reporters were the exceptions on that score.)

As the dinner got under way, David walked up to the dais to see an official who was handling the publicity for the event and asked him if there was anything he should know that might not have been sent out in the advance release. He was told no.

David started to walk back to the press table when he noticed, sitting at a table right below the dais, a face that looked familiar.

"I know that man—but who is he?" David said to himself, stopping short. He walked closer to the man's table. "Of course —that's Fred Carstairs!"

David had never before seen the man in person, but he had seen his picture in the *Ledger* and the other newspapers scores of times. The pictures, he thought, did not do the racketeer justice. His nose was not nearly as large, and, in fact, seen in the flesh, he was a rather handsome, almost distinguished-looking individual—though his jacket was too heavily padded at the shoulders.

All the tables were numbered—and Carstairs was at number four. Along with the press release which David had, there was also a separate printed sheet, which gave the seating arrangements—who was sitting where. David looked at the seating list.

For table number four—with ten seats—it gave the names and full titles of nine men. Six were among the most prominent judges in the city. Of the other three, two were the leaders of the opposing political parties in the county and the third was a fiscal advisor to the state's governor. Carstairs' name was not on the list.

The nine men seated with him deferred to Carstairs as though he were a visiting crown prince. They vied for his attention, and several of them got up from their seats, walked up to his chair and whispered in his ear. Carstairs seemed to be doing very little talking.

Soon there were other men coming up to him from all over the room.

"Hello, Fred, glad you could make it," or words to that effect, each visitor said to the racketeer, who received this homage placidly, as though it were his due.

Even though the list in David's hands listed the nine men scheduled to be at table number four, he did not know for certain whether the men present were the same as those who were on the list. He thereupon returned to the dais and again sought out the man handling the publicity.

"I wanted to check some names with you," he said.

"Sure."

David pointed to the nine names listed for table four and asked if those were the men seated there.

"Yes, of course they are. Don't you know them personally?"

"No," David replied. "One more thing. Isn't that tenth man Fred Carstairs?" He managed to make his voice sound casual.

The publicity man glanced sharply at David and said casually, "Sure. That's Carstairs."

"Well, his name is not on the seating list at all—for any table."

"Obviously, a printer's oversight. It should have been."

"Oh," David said, "has he been active in this $1,000,000 drive?"

The publicity man looked at his questioner with great sur-

prise. "Of course he has. He not only has been one of our
biggest contributors, but he's personally responsible for the
attendance of most of the prominent people here tonight. We
are terribly indebted to him."

"Thank you," David said and returned to the press table.

Suppressing his excitement, he pointed out to the *Transcript*
reporter what was going on—this obeisance to Carstairs by
judges and politicians—and what the publicity man had told
him.

"So what?" the *Transcript* reporter said. "I can't get excited
about that. This is a good cause, isn't it?"

David hurried through his meal and scurried to Carstairs'
table. Dignified looking men were still approaching the prominent racketeer. A few minutes after they had returned to their
respective tables, David walked up to each of them separately,
identified himself and said blandly, "Sir, I just wanted to make
sure that this seating list is correct. We'll probably run in the
Ledger many names of the more prominent persons attending
this affair."

In that way, David got the name of every judge and official
who went over to pay his respects to Carstairs—long known
as an unofficial judge-maker and political power behind the
scenes.

The speeches, fortunately, were short—and also dull. They
contributed nothing. David rushed back across town to the
Ledger office.

Platt was doing something at his own desk when David
walked in. As the latter sat down, to go over his notes, Platt
said: "Hey, Davey. Looks like, after all these years, they want
to make a foreign correspondent out of me!"

"You serious? Where you going?"

"I don't know that I'm going anywhere. But they want to
send me to the Paris bureau, to take the place of Hairston,
who's taking a leave to write a book or something."

"Paris! Boy, do I envy you!"

"My wife wants to go in the worst way. But I like New York and can live without Paris. I'd rather be considered a pretty good general reporter around here, concentrating on crime, than just another foreign correspondent. Besides, I'm not so sure I can handle it. Well, we'll see, though frankly my wife usually gets what she wants. . . . How was the dinner— chicken again?"

"No. Prime ribs of beef."

Platt whistled. "Not bad!"

"I think I have a pretty good yarn here, Red."

"Oh? What's up?"

"Well, I just saw practically every judge and leading politician in town curtsy for your boy, Fred Carstairs."

"What are you talking about?"

David explained.

"Did you check those names out? Did you make sure the people who sat with Carstairs and came up to him from other tables were the same ones printed on that seating list?"

"I certainly did!"

"Did you report to Holloway yet?"

"I was just about to—but first I was going to look at my notes."

"Let's go."

With that, Platt rushed David over to the city desk and said to Holloway: "You got a bright one here. Listen to what David has to tell you."

"What other papers were there?" Holly asked after getting a fill in.

"Only the *Transcript*."

"Who covered for them?"

"Page—Arthur Page."

"Does he have what you have?"

"No, he didn't seem interested."

"Good! His paper will be when they see the *Ledger*. Let 'er roll—and slug it 'Carstairs.' Print every name you're sure of —with their full titles. Be sure to give the names of the nine guys sitting with the racketeer. Oh, if we only had pictures!"

The *Ledger* story created a sensation. Other newspapers were at first fearful of picking it up—since they had no proof of their own that these officials had either been at the affair or had gone up to Carstairs.

About noon of the day that the *Ledger* story appeared, Carstairs called up Platt.

"What gives, Red?" he asked plaintively. "This man, David White—why did he print that story?"

"Was it true, Fred?"

"Sure it was true. But this was for a good cause. I helped them raise a lot of dough. I think that's the important thing. So what if these famous people came up and spoke to me? They've been good friends for years."

"Fred, you're a smart cookie—but you never did know what makes a good news story. And look—if you get into any more trouble with the local cops or the Feds, this same David White will probably be covering it. My wife tells me we're going to Paris."

☆☆☆ 23

DAVID IS OFFERED A BRIBE

PARTICULARLY WHEN COVERING TRIALS, David found that his abbreviations and privately evolved shorthand were invaluable.

In the first place, the official transcript of the court proceedings was not typed up until after the close of the morning or afternoon session—and David did not have time to wait for that. In the second place, the transcript was an expensive proposition—there was a charge of so much per page, and it was not a good idea for a reporter to run up unnecessary expenses.

The greatest hazard of court reporting was, surprisingly enough, boredom. This was due to the number of lawyers who maundered endlessly and repeated themselves constantly.

This was also true of a number of judges and district attorneys. Whether through an actual disability to express themselves concisely, or an infatuation with the sound of their own voices, they droned on endlessly. It was an old and well-known situation.

"If I had my way," Holloway once told him, "I would make it mandatory for all members of the bar to take a course in English before actually permitting them to practice. There are too many of them who use one hundred and fifty words to say what could be said in ten words—and much plainer, too. Many lawyers could use a good rewrite man."

One of the most successful lawyers in town was Daniel D. Brothers. He had built up quite a record. He specialized in handling notorious crimes, and through his skill in cross-examination had won acquittal for his clients in several cases which the public had expected to end in convictions.

"When you're in real trouble, hire Dan Brothers," was an often heard expression.

David had been covering courts a short time when he ran into Brothers. The lawyer was representing a small-time hoodlum who was being tried for shooting and seriously injuring a patrolman who caught him in the act of holding up a gas station. The hoodlum managed to get away, but his license plate number was seen and he was captured within an hour.

This was the opening day of the trial, and David, following the advice that Platt had given him to get acquainted with all the principals in a case, went up and introduced himself to Brothers. This was just outside of court, which was due to open in a few minutes.

Brothers was most charming. He gripped David's hand firmly, asked him how long he had been at the *Ledger,* how he liked it, then said, "If you have any questions, don't hesitate to call on me."

Brothers' client, who had a lengthy police record from several previous scrapes with the law, had been receiving up to now a not exactly favorable press. The shooting of the police officer had been a page 1 story in all the papers, and there had been editorials on how this case typified the growing lawlessness in the city.

Brothers knew that it would be a tough one. During the selection of the jury, David noticed, the lawyer probed deeply into the background of each person he examined and especially concentrated on whether they had any relatives—regardless of how remote—connected in any way with any kind of law enforcement agency. He explained he was referring to any level—local, state or federal.

Finally, a jury was picked, consisting of twelve men. This was at the end of a long day—and David rushed out of court, headed back for the *Ledger,* in order to write his story.

"Hi, Dave," Brothers said, a restraining hand on the young reporter's shoulder. "How does the jury look to you?"

"Looks like a good, impartial one."

There was some more talk along those lines, then Brothers reached into his jacket handkerchief pocket, pulled out a cigar, slipped it into David's jacket, wheeled around and walked away with the farewell, "See you in court tomorrow."

It all happened so fast that David had not had time to say, "I don't smoke." But it was getting late, and he headed down into the subway.

He did not remember that he had the cigar until after he

had finished writing his story and was about to leave the office for the evening with Alice. They were to have dinner together and then take in a movie.

He knew that Holloway was a cigar smoker, though it seemed that the city editor preferred to chew on a cigar, rather than smoke it. In fact, David had noticed, Holloway sometimes kept an unlit cigar in his mouth for an hour and often used it as a pointer.

"Here's a gift from Brothers," David said, handing over the cigar.

"Thanks, Dave. Coming from him, it should be a good one." Holly removed the dead wad of a cigar from his mouth and discarded it in a wastepaper basket. "I'm about ready for a change in flavor now."

With that, Holloway removed the cellophane wrapper, and then, like all habitual cigar smokers, began to remove the cigar band.

"Hey—look at this!" he called.

David looked. He saw something which appeared to be green—and folded over and over again. "What is it?" he asked.

"Wait'll I open it up and see!"

Holloway put the fresh cigar down on his desk, next to his oversized scissors and paste pot. He unfolded the green piece of paper.

"It's a twenty-dollar bill!" he exclaimed. "What do you know!"

David stood there, openmouthed.

"Is that supposed to be a bribe?" he finally asked, incredulous.

"Well," the city editor said dryly, "it is in the realm of possibility, I suppose, that the manufacturer of this cigar is trying to promote trade by giving away twenty-dollar bills. Highly unlikely—but possible."

"What do I do now?" David asked.

Holloway looked at the twenty-dollar bill for a few seconds without answering and then came to a decision.

"By George, we'll make a philanthropist out of that lawyer, that's what!" He chuckled with anticipatory amusement. "Wait'll he gets his receipt! David—take that bill over to the Country Fund as a donation from Brothers. Get a receipt and make sure they print his name, along with the other donors, in the daily list."

The Country Fund was the *Ledger's* privately promoted charity, through which poor city children who would otherwise be unable to leave the hot city streets in the summertime were enabled to spend a week or two in the country, thanks to the donations of *Ledger* readers.

David did as he was bid—and even managed to keep a straight face when the elderly lady who was in charge of the Country Fund promotion clucked happily and said, "My, that was nice of Mr. Brothers!"

David spent an uneasy evening with Alice, who was incredulous at this turn of events. "You mean in this day and age that lawyer had the temerity to offer an open bribe?" she asked. "What did he hope to get from you?"

David smiled at her indulgently. "He expected value in return, you goose. A favorable story on his client."

"For a measly twenty dollars?" Alice laughed wickedly. "Now if he had made it two thousand . . ." They both laughed.

David got to court early the next morning and sought out Brothers as he stepped off the eleventh-floor elevator. With the attorney was an associate counsel, who was assisting him in the case.

In his hands, David held a copy of the *Ledger,* folded to the Country Fund page, on which appeared a daily box listing the contributors and the amount of each donation. He had circled Brothers' name and the twenty dollars attributed to him. He also had a receipt made out to the attorney.

"On behalf of the *Ledger's* Country Fund, my city editor has asked me to thank you," said David casually as he handed Brothers the two items.

Puzzled, the lawyer looked at the paper and receipt and then, as realization flooded him, he turned a bright pink, for, in the few, noncommittal words David spoke, Brothers understood that his attempted bribe had failed, and that, furthermore, the city editor had been notified. His name was now dirt at the *Ledger*.

Brothers' associate counsel, aware of the emotional currents he was a witness to, but unaware of their cause, was bewildered, but he followed obediently when Brothers abruptly said, "Let's go," and walked off.

David followed them leisurely into the courtroom, smiling quietly.

The trial continued for a week. In their few subsequent conversations, Brothers never referred to the twenty-dollar incident, nor did David mention it. Brothers, in fact, avoided the young *Ledger* reporter, which was not too surprising. His client was convicted.

☆☆☆ *24*

DAVID LEARNS ABOUT GRAND JURIES

ONE OF THE MORE NOTORIOUS crimes which rocked the city was the shooting and attempted assassination of Larry Larchmont, the respectable owner of a snack bar frequented by high-school students. When the story broke, Holloway assigned David to cover it.

Like most such teen-age hang-outs, Larchmont's had a juke box. Unknown to the owner, however, the music box had been placed there by a racketeer, Lefty Kane, who had a police record as long as his arm. Kane had been in many rackets through the years, and when one petered out, he turned to another. Each time he prudently retreated farther in the background, leaving the younger hoodlums to "front" them. He was now in a position where he controlled the placing of juke boxes and, by threat and coercion, was collecting a sum from the owner of each establishment which was far in excess of the juke box's earnings.

Whenever any of the customers threatened to be "difficult," one of the boys paid him a visit. The "host" rarely acted up again; in fact, the visitor must have been very persuasive indeed—the victims never even complained to the police.

But this was before Larchmont. Larry Larchmont was a very stubborn man. He not only refused to be cowed by his visitor; he told the thug if he ever saw him again, he'd call the police.

And so one night, as he was closing his shop, Larchmont was grabbed from the rear, forced into an automobile and driven to the outskirts of town. Two bullets were pumped into him and he was left for dead.

Miraculously, he did not die, and, after a lengthy stay in the hospital, he recovered. The police, acting "on information," picked up a young hoodlum named Rocky Masters, who was known to be one of Kane's goons. While the police were interested in getting Masters as the actual assailant, they were even more interested in working up a case against Kane as the mastermind of the plot.

The district attorney made all kinds of promises to Masters, the principal one being that, if he went before a grand jury and told all he knew about Kane, he (Masters) would be allowed to plead to a lesser charge and wind up with a short jail term or even a suspended sentence.

"We are not interested in you especially," Masters was told. "We know that Kane was behind this—and we want him."

Masters was fairly young, and the thought of spending the best years of his life behind bars must have momentarily dulled his thinking. He agreed to go before the grand jury and, led by the district attorney, walked through the door into a room where twenty-three men and women sat in secret session.

It was at this point that David decided to have some legal points clarified. While he knew, in a vague sort of way, about grand juries, he wanted some solid facts, so he made a telephone call to the law offices of Judge Ezra Steiner and made an appointment to see him later that afternoon.

Once a man has served on the bench, he retains the title of "judge"—by common courtesy—for the rest of his days. But few men deserved that honor so much as did Judge Steiner. He had served on the bench of a federal court for eight years at a high personal financial loss before returning to his lucrative private practice.

During his tenure on the bench, colleagues from various courts had come to him with knotty legal problems they were unable to unravel. Unofficially, he was considered the "Supreme Court" of judges, since he was never once reversed by a higher court. Unlike the great majority of lawyers David knew, Judge Steiner was never verbose. He had a wonderful perception—was able to get to the crux of a problem immediately and hold it up to the light of logic and law. He was one of the few men David had ever met who could make the law exciting and alive.

Judge Steiner was a justly famous man around the courts, and while David had heard of him even while he was a copy boy, he had only met him a week before. Expecting a jurist in the fine old tradition, dashing in appearance and with a leonine head, David had been taken aback when he was introduced to

a thin little rail of a man, with eyes as sharp as a bird's. After expressing his pleasure at meeting him (which the unassuming judge met with an inquiring, surprised manner), David had inquired whether he might call on the judge when in need of information. The spare little lawyer smiled happily. "Any time, my boy. I am always delighted to dispense knowledge; it is ignorance that distresses me."

And so, while the small-time thug was singing to the grand jury, David sat in the well-appointed offices of Judge Ezra Steiner and plied him with questions.

"Who picks the grand jury?"

"The judge. They are ordinary citizens selected from a pool."

"How long do they serve?"

"As a general rule, for one month. It depends on the intricacy of the case. One grand jury in a large gambling investigation stayed on for four years—but that was most unusual."

"Exactly what is the function of the grand jury?"

"To decide whether there is good reason to believe that one or more persons has committed a crime." Judge Steiner paused. "But it is also there to make sure that the innocent are not charged with a crime. The district attorney presents his evidence and, acting upon it, the grand jury can issue subpoenas to get witnesses, books and records before it."

"Then they listen to the evidence and, on the basis of what is presented to them, they decide whether or not there shall be a trial?"

"Yes, and if they decide a trial is in order, they will vote an indictment. Should they decide, on the other hand, that the evidence is not sufficient, the suspect is cleared."

"Well, then," pursued David, "the district attorney is the big wheel here. The grand jury knows only what he'll tell them. Doesn't this place a tremendous amount of power in the d.a.'s hands?"

Judge Steiner smiled. "Don't ever underestimate the intelligence of the common man. The grand jury is an extremely powerful group, and any time they don't happen to like the way the d.a. is conducting an investigation, they can order him out of the room and take over the questioning themselves."

"Does that happen often?" asked David.

"Not often, because we have had honorable men in the job for a number of years. But it has happened. Some time ago, we had a runaway grand jury—that is, they 'ran away' from the district attorney. They were dissatisfied with the paltry amount of evidence he was presenting in the investigation of a rather corrupt situation. As a direct result of their recommendations to the presiding judge, the d.a. was relieved of his duties in this particular matter and a special prosecutor was appointed by the governor."

"That must have been quite a scandal," said David. "What happened to the d.a.?"

"Well," Judge Steiner laughed, "it was not the best publicity in the world. He was not reelected."

"Must all twenty-three members of a grand jury concur unanimously before an indictment can be voted?" David asked next.

"Oh, no. Only a majority—or twelve. Because many of them are businessmen, and must sit for at least a month, it isn't possible for them to attend all sessions. Therefore, a quorum is considered sixteen members—meaning that for a grand jury to sit, at least sixteen must be present. But to vote an indictment, not a majority of sixteen, but a majority of the total strength, or twelve, must vote to indict. An indictment is a formal accusation, whereby the grand jury says in effect, 'we think that you are guilty of a crime, and we order you to stand trial before a petit jury.' "

David asked, "Is an appearance before a grand jury voluntary?"

"No—it's mandatory."

"But how can that be?" puzzled David. "You can't force a man to testify against himself."

"Of course not. But it's very rare that a potential defendant would ever be asked to go before a grand jury. If he were, the odds are that the d.a. is after bigger fish, and the defendant has either been promised immunity from prosecution or else a 'deal' has been made in advance—that is, the d.a. has promised to prosecute under a lesser charge in exchange for his cooperation."

"How can one find out what went on in the grand jury room?"

"You cannot. The happenings in the grand jury room are extremely secret, so that the person under investigation will not know the nature of the testimony against him. Also, so that the innocent will not walk under a cloud."

"Under what circumstances may grand jury testimony be used in a trial?"

"Usually when a witness gives a trial jury a version which is in conflict with what he told the grand jury."

"What if a witness should die after he testifies before the grand jury—and before he can repeat that testimony in court?"

"That would be too bad. It is as though he never said anything. That is one reason why police put important witnesses in protective custody after they have given damaging information before a grand jury."

"Supposing a witness has a change of heart, and after spilling the beans before the grand jury, has a 'loss of memory' at the trial?"

"It happens every day," sighed Judge Steiner. "Of course, any 'deal' with the district attorney is thereupon abrogated. The judge can, and very often does, hold the witness in contempt for refusing to answer the questions and an additional sentence in the form of a fine and/or term in jail is imposed."

A very grateful David got to his feet and thanked the judge profusely. "Not at all," the judge's eyes twinkled, "at least now I know I'll never read in any of your stories that 'John Doe was convicted by a grand jury'!"

"But that's an impossible statement!" cried David, aghast.

"Fine!" said the little jurist, laughing. "You've learned your lesson well!"

Back at Criminal Courts, David found out that the grand jury had indicted not only Masters, but Lefty Kane, as well. That meant that Masters must have given the grand jury more than enough incriminating testimony against his boss. This was verified when the district attorney let it be known that Lefty Kane was going to be tried for attempted murder, and Masters would plead guilty to the lesser crime of assault.

As a general rule, it takes about six months between the time the grand jury votes an indictment and the start of the trial, but public feeling ran high on the brutality of the attack on Larchmont and the trial was scheduled to begin very soon.

When the trial began, it became evident the moment Masters walked into the courtroom that he had had a change of heart. Kane, he now said, had had nothing to do with the attack on Larchmont. When the grand jury minutes were read to him, he professed surprise. He didn't recall ever having said any such thing, and if he had—it wasn't true. The trial of Lefty Kane collapsed.

Masters was thereupon put on trial for attempted murder, and David covered that as well.

Larchmont could not positively identify his assailant—it was night, and he was grabbed from the back. But Masters was, in effect, hoist by his own petard. Before he had entered the grand jury room, and while in the midst of making his deal with the d.a., he had signed a statement for the police, admitting his part in the Larchmont attack and also implicating

Kane. This statement was introduced into the court record by the d.a.—over the bitter objections of defense counsel—and proved Masters' undoing.

The trial jury convicted Masters of attempted murder. It took only a single ballot to reach this verdict.

A few days later, Masters was up for sentence. The judge gave him a chance to save himself from a severe sentence by admitting—even at this late date—his part in the crime, and implicating Kane. Specifically, the judge wanted him to repeat in open court what he had testified to in secret before the grand jury. This, Masters refused to do.

"You," the judge told Masters, "are the victim of underworld lockjaw. You obviously have been reached and warned, and you have decided to obey the law of the underworld. This, despite the fact that the court promises you protection. So be it. But I will show you that the underworld will not dictate to this court. I hereby sentence you to thirty years in state prison."

Masters, glum, was led away. He had been convicted and sentenced, all right, but the key figure in the attack was still at large. Kane was out on bail on his indictment for the crime.

David went up to the judge's chambers.

"What happens now?" asked David. "Can the state still prosecute Kane?"

"I'm afraid not," the judge replied.

"Why not? There's still a grand jury indictment against him, isn't there?" David pursued.

"Oh, yes," sighed the judge. "But in all probability it will have to be dismissed—unless Masters has a change of heart and decides to testify against Kane. But I doubt it. Let's be realistic." He faced David squarely. "Let's assume that Masters talked, and I wiped out his sentence. His life would be worthless! He feels he would rather stay healthy in jail for the rest of his life than lead a so-called 'free' life which might well be wiped out by a bullet at any time."

"And Kane continues to operate," David said flatly.

"I'm afraid so. But that's the rule of evidence. There is no question but that Kane was the mastermind of this attempted murder. But, so far, the state is unable to prove it—legally."

☆☆☆ *25*

A DOUBLE HOMICIDE

DAVID HAD BEEN so busy at the courts that he realized with a start one Monday that it was almost six months since he had last visited the east side precinct which had been his stamping grounds in his days at the shack.

He was in no mood for a movie and Alice was, of course, working. It seemed an ideal opportunity to renew old acquaintances.

As he walked into the familiar, high-ceilinged room, he was greeted cordially by Lieutenant McCarthy at the desk. "Hi, Dave—long time no see! What brings you here?"

"I got lonesome for you and Terry Mulligan," teased David.

"Boy, you must be desperate—and psychic. Mulligan got in only ten minutes ago. He's upstairs."

"I'll go up and shoot the breeze with him," said David, "that is, if he's free?"

"As free as he ever is—you know Terry. Go ahead up." With a wave, the lieutenant returned to his papers. David walked up the stairs of the old building and opened the door to the squad room. There, amid the usual welter of cigar butts and ashes, was Terry Mulligan. He was tilted precariously back on his chair, his feet up on the desk, one eye half-closed against the heavy, blue cigar smoke spiralling upward from the stogie at the side of his mouth. The chair crashed back into position as the lithe detective got to his feet and extended his hand to David.

"Hello, boy! Come on in and sit down. Good to see you!"

"Thanks, Terry—it's good to be here. Feels like old times. Doing anything exciting?"

"Maybe," replied Mulligan cryptically.

"Oh?" David kept his voice on a casual level. "What's up?"

"You read the paper today?"

"I think so." David removed a folded *Ledger* from his jacket pocket and skimmed through the pages.

"The double death—the doctor and his wife—over on the west side," said Mulligan helpfully.

"The brandy suicide pact?" David asked. "I read that story." He thumbed through the *Ledger* to the page on which the story was located and read it through once again.

The story was headed:

PHYSICIAN, WIFE
TAKE OWN LIVES

It was a tragic story, involving Dr. Charles Foster, attached to several hospitals, and his wife, Frances, a dietician. They had been married for twenty-five years and, so far as their neighbors knew, they were a deeply devoted couple.

Their bodies had been discovered by their only child, George, twenty-three, a tall, ascetic-looking youth who was an amateur poet. He had returned home early Sunday morning and found his father sprawled on the kitchen floor and his mother in the bedroom. Each was clutching an empty brandy glass. Their faces were dreadfully contorted. He called the police.

No notes were found. An autopsy disclosed that the couple

had downed brandy, spiked with cyanide. They had died, according to the medical examiner, within five minutes.

It was an apparent suicide pact.

"What about it?" asked David. "These things happen. Both of them had ready access to lethal drugs. Perhaps one or both had a malignant disease?"

"No," replied Mulligan. "They were in excellent physical shape."

"How was their mental shape? Lots of people have fits of great depression sometimes. Isn't it possible that, feeling real low, they decided to end their lives?"

"It's possible all right—but I doubt it. We had the son in for questioning—purely routine, you know. He couldn't imagine why. We questioned the neighbors—they'd lived in that apartment almost twenty years—as well as some relatives. They were all shocked. The Fosters were a happy, well-adjusted couple who simply were not the type who'd kill themselves."

"You know what the medicos say," David broke in. "That's the type that generally does it."

"I know," replied Mulligan thoughtfully. "I can't put my finger on it, but there's something about the whole thing I don't like. If it was a suicide pact, why weren't they in the same room? True, they don't always do it that way—sometimes they don't want to watch each other suffer. I don't know—maybe I've been on the job too many years—you know, one can get too suspicious.

"I went along to the funeral this morning," he continued. "The son was really overwrought. The relatives had to pull him back; he tried to jump into the open graves. They practically had to carry him to the car."

David eyed Mulligan closely. "It's the son that's bothering you, isn't it?"

Terry nodded slowly. "Something about that boy that isn't

quite right. Here you have a big, hulking kid of twenty-three, who graduated from college two years ago and has never had a job. He writes poetry! Also, he combs his hair all day. . . . Well," he turned back to his desk, "excuse me, Dave. I've got to check out a couple of things."

David got up to leave, but his interest had been whetted. "Terry, can I call you tomorrow?" he asked.

"Wednesday should be better," said Mulligan significantly. "Have coffee with me late in the afternoon—five or so."

"I'll be here," David promised.

David telephoned Holloway the next morning and told him what was up. "By all means keep that date," said Holly, "and let me know what happens."

By prearrangement, David met Mulligan in a tea shoppe three blocks from the precinct. It was not a place where they were likely to meet anyone they knew.

"This is a murder," Terry stated blandly.

"Are you sure?"

"Sure as rain," said Mulligan confidently. Then he filled David in on the current—and highly secret—investigation.

"I checked the joint bank account and safe deposit box of the parents. They had $30,000 on deposit and the father carried life insurance totaling $50,000. Nothing unusual about that, but I think what bothered me was that the bodies were hardly cold in the grave when the life insurance company called me up. The son, George, had showed up to collect on the policy. Of course, they couldn't pay it until they got an official document attesting to the death of his parents, and they asked me to send it along. I stalled them—told them I was tied up, but I'd send it along in a week or so.

"Then I went to the savings bank where the Fosters kept their $30,000. This money was in a three-way account— which means any one of the three could have withdrawn it. I got there too late—George had closed out the account and mumbled something about buying an expensive sports car and shipping it to Europe, where he hoped to settle down.

"Boy!" Mulligan paused and wiped his forehead with a handkerchief. "For a minute there I had a tough time. I asked the bank man what kind of car, and he couldn't remember. I mentioned about five and finally one rang a bell. I left and hotfooted it over to the agency. There's only one in the city. At eight thousand bucks a car," he interrupted himself wryly, "you can imagine that they do a rushing business! Anyway, the salesman at the agency confirmed that George Foster bought one of their cars and arranged with them to send it to Europe. Fortunately, the ship isn't due to sail for a week."

"But what about the son," interrupted David impatiently. "Did you talk with him?"

"Hold your horses—I'll get to that," returned Terry amiably. "Yes, I went up to the apartment—and almost fell through the floor. George himself answered the bell, as cordial as you please. You would never have imagined there was a death in the family. He was mine host—and he had a boy friend there. Both of them were drinking champagne and had been at it for a while. There were two empty bottles, and they'd just broken open a third. They offered me a drink, and I took it. It's not often I get into champagne circles, you know," he added apologetically. "It was good, too. Anyway, I'm introduced to the boy friend, Perry Norton, a good-looking kid, about the same age as George.

"I apologized for intruding on this scene of domestic felicity —although I didn't put it that way—and asked him if he would tell me once more the exact circumstances under which he found his parents.

"So he did. Only this time he mentioned for the first time that Perry had accompanied him to the apartment the night he found his parents, and he also said that he and Perry were going to Europe to live. I should mention that both these lads were a wee bit high from the giggly water. Of course, I didn't crack when he broke the news that Perry was with him that night—just asked them some more casual questions.

"Then I got up to leave, and, sort of as an afterthought, I asked them whether they wouldn't like to come down to the precinct with me. I still had the papers to fill out for the parents' insurance, and I mentioned I could give these to them and get it over with. Of course, they came."

"Well, where are they now?" David was quite excited.

"Right there in the precinct," replied Terry laconically, "singing."

"What?" David's voice rose an octave. "They killed them?"

"When I got them there, I took George into one room, and my partner took Perry into another. Within an hour, the story was out."

David made a move to rise. "What am I doing here then? I've got to get to a phone!"

"Sit down, Davey. You can't get anything officially until the reports are all typed and the confessions are signed. No exclusive this time—but you can't complain that I didn't fill you in!"

Reluctantly, David relaxed in his chair. "How much longer?" he asked.

"About half an hour. I'll take you back in time, don't worry. You want to hear the rest, or don't you?" he asked belligerently.

"Sure I do."

"George didn't like his parents, to put it mildly. It seems, ever since he was a kid, his mother called him a sissy and taunted him because he read books. She always threw it up to him that he acted more like a girl than a boy. While his father didn't join in, the doctor was obviously under his wife's domination. All he ever said was, 'Do what your mother says. She's right.'

"George told me he got real good marks in composition and literature in high school and even tried writing some plays. His mother tore up everything he wrote and threw the typewriter out. She replaced it with a baseball glove and a bat.

"He had a number of different jobs, but he says he hated them all and quit—never stayed more than a day or two. It drove his mother crazy. Then he decided he wanted to go to Europe and his mother threatened to throw him out of the apartment altogether—without a cent. So he talked things over with his friend, Perry Norton. Perry majored in chemistry and knew several places where they could buy cyanide without any trouble. They got some. A few nights after his mother had threatened to throw him out, George came into the apartment with a bottle of imported brandy. He told the folks he'd gotten a job he was crazy about, that his wandering days were over, and suggested they have a drink to celebrate.

"He went into the kitchen and got three brandy glasses, put cyanide in two of them and brought 'em out, filled with brandy. They all drank a happy toast—and the parents collapsed almost immediately.

"His friend Perry had been waiting in the hall, and George now let him in. They moved one body into the kitchen and the other into the bedroom, washed and dried the glass George drank out of and left the apartment. They dropped the remaining cyanide down a street sewer."

Mulligan looked at his watch. "I guess we can go now."

There was no trial. Psychiatrists who examined George Foster were of the unanimous opinion that his was an advanced case of dementia praecox. He was committed to a mental institution for the criminal insane. His friend, Perry Norton, was found to be quite sane. Since he was in on the plot to murder the Fosters, even though he did not actually do the deed, he was considered equally culpable under the law. He pleaded guilty to second degree murder and was sentenced to from twenty years to life imprisonment.

"I have a question," David said to Mulligan when both defendants had been sent away. "What happens to that money George took out of the bank and the $50,000 life insurance left by his father? Who gets it?"

"It will be held in escrow for the rest of his life. If he ever recovers his sanity, all that money will go to him. I might add that the dealer who sold him that car took it back and returned the money."

"Isn't he subject to trial for the murders if he ever recovers his sanity?"

"Yes, but I have never heard of a case where a person has recovered his sanity and is then brought to trial. Legally, they're supposed to stand trial. Actually, they never do."

✧✧✧ *26*

POLICEMEN AND POLICEWOMEN

WHILE COVERING THE COURTS, David frequently had occasion to go over to Police Headquarters, to get additional background material for a story. For instance, if the defendant had had previous skirmishes with the law, David would check his police record, or "yellow sheet" as it is known. (The record is listed on yellow paper.)

Since Police Headquarters was only four short blocks from the Criminal Courts building, he made it a practice to drop in regularly to ask, "What's new?"

The question was generally put to Wesley Foote, the department's spokesman, who had the title of Director of Community and Public Relations for the Police Department. An ex-newspaperman, Foote was not impressed with his title and knew his job thoroughly. When secrecy was imposed upon him, he gave no information rather than misinformation. Having worked on the other side of the fence, he knew what data was expected of him, and he supplied it—whenever he could.

One afternoon, when David dropped by and asked the inevitable question, Foote handed him a fact sheet, which was titled "source document for personnel data card." On it was printed almost every conceivable kind of occupation and skill.

"What's this?" asked David.

"The Department is starting to use that new electronic brain machine, you know, the selector kind of thing, where you feed it a whole mass of data and then, when you want to know something, you press the right buttons and out it comes! Every member of the police force has filled in one of these sheets, which we translate into punched cards. Then, if we want a cop who speaks Vietnamese, say, or is a metallurgist or a cowpuncher or a masseur—we ask the machine, and out come the names. Before this, if we wanted any specialized skill in a hurry, we'd have to send a teletype to each of the eighty-five stations and the captain would have to interview every one of his men." Foote paused a moment, then asked rhapsodically, "Isn't it a wonderful age we're living in?"

"Sure is," replied David. He skimmed through the more than four hundred questions listed. "Boy, you haven't left anything out! Let's see—you have any policemen who speak Chinese?"

"Probably. We have almost everything else. Let's ask the machine."

As they walked toward the statistical room, David asked, "Are the policewomen operating the machines?"

Surprised, Foote replied, "No, why should they?"

"I don't know—I sort of assumed the women would do the clerical jobs, to free the able-bodied men for more arduous tasks."

"There are comparatively few able-bodied policemen in clerical jobs," Foote told him. "Most of the men in here have more than fifteen years in the job, and the great majority of them have some service-incurred disabilities. As for the police-women—well, you have a lot to learn. Supposing you go around and have a talk with some of them. As a matter of fact, they're rehearsing for their annual show this week, right here in the line-up room, so, if you can't make it today, drop around tomorrow."

By this time, they had come abreast of a huge monster of a machine, which was clacking away. At the moment, it was slipping into a pocket the card of every officer who could speak Spanish.

"Joe!" Foote called to a policeman-clerk who was operating the machine. "We got any boys who speak Chinese?"

"I think so," replied the clerk. He put a large stack of cards into the mechanism and pushed a few buttons. Out popped twenty-eight cards. Twenty-seven names were obviously of Chinese descent, but the twenty-eighth card bore the name Sean McGlincy.

"Sean McGlincy speaks Chinese?" David asked incredulously.

"Maybe the machine made a mistake," said Foote. "Or else McGlincy isn't his real name. Only way you can find out is to get McGlincy himself." He glanced at the card. "It says here he's attached to the eleventh precinct."

David telephoned the precinct. McGlincy was on foot patrol, but would be calling in to the desk lieutenant shortly. David left word for McGlincy to call him, which he did within ten minutes.

David explained that he had seen a demonstration of the new selector machine and that McGlincy's name popped out among those who could speak Chinese.

"Was it an error or do you really speak Chinese?" asked David.

"It's no error—I speak it fluently," replied the police officer.

"Were you always known as Sean McGlincy?"

"Yes."

"Where were you born?"

"In Manhattan, off Chinatown. I grew up with Chinese kids. I've also been on patrol with Chinese police officers. I can speak it as well as they can."

"Say something in Chinese."

McGlincy obliged. The unfamiliar singsong cadence, of course, meant nothing to David. "What was that you said?" he asked.

"Cops don't make enough dough," translated McGlincy, chuckling.

David decided to go back to the *Ledger* and write his business-machine piece while he had the feel of it. The policewomen could wait. He wrote an amusing tongue-in-cheek article on the mechanization of the police department and wound up with the McGlincy colloquy.

Back at Police Headquarters the following afternoon, Foote complimented him on the story. "It had a nice, light touch."

"Thanks," said David. "I came back to see the policewomen in action."

"This is hardly typical of their day." Foote laughed. "But you'll see more of them now than you would in ordinary circumstances." His eyebrows arched skyward.

They had been walking toward the line-up room and when they arrived there, David laughed aloud. "I see what you mean."

Most of the policewomen were in light rehearsal attire—
some in bathing suits, others in leotards. They were earnestly
practising a precision dance routine and they looked as attractive and adept as professionals. David made a comment to
that effect to Wesley Foote.

"That shouldn't surprise you," replied Foote. "Lots of them
have had to take jobs in night clubs in the course of their jobs
as policewomen. When we have a complaint about a club, the
best way to get the goods on them is by planting somebody inside. A pretty girl with a good figure can always get a job—
either in the chorus or as a cigarette girl.

"Come on—I'll introduce you to Mary Stewart, who's running this production. She's been a cop for a long time and
knows more about policewomen than I do. Besides, I've got to
get back to work."

He steered David over to a dark-haired, middle-aged
woman, who was obviously in charge. She was deep in budget
problems with two members of the chorus line. She was saying, "Who ever heard of a cancan costume without lace?"
They nodded in agreement, and one of them replied, "O.K.
We'll get the money from the tuxedo. We'll save about ten
dollars by not renting one. Somebody's husband is sure to
have an old one in the closet."

As the two young women walked off, Foote made the introduction. "Mary, this is Dave White of the *Ledger*. He wants
to know about policewomen, so help him out. Dave, Mary
Stewart knows more about lady cops than anyone. Her father
was a policeman, her husband is one, and she's been with the
department almost twenty years." He turned to David. "Drop
by on your way out, if you have the time," he said, and walked
back toward his own office.

David turned to Mrs. Stewart. "Are many of the policewomen service-connected? I mean, were their fathers or brothers in the department—or their husbands?" he asked.

"Quite a few," admitted the dark-eyed woman. "After all, it's the most natural thing in the world, if you've been listening to your father or big brother talk about his job at home, for you to get interested also. Sometimes it works the opposite way, though—where the father, who is a policeman, is much against his daughter's going on the force. But you know the old story—where there's a will, there's a way." She smiled.

"Where do you get your recruits from?"

"They have every conceivable background—they're ex-teachers, ex-social workers, ex-nurses, ex-secretaries."

"What lures them into police work?"

"What lured you into newspaper work?" countered Mrs. Stewart.

David laughed. "Certainly not the money," he said.

"That goes double in spades here," replied Mrs. Stewart with feeling. "As a matter of fact, that's a very touchy thing with us. The city fathers, for reasons best known to themselves, will not allow women to take a civil service examination for a higher rating. We're stopped dead at policewomen, which is the same pay as a patrolman."

"That's the highest you can go?" David was incredulous.

"For the most part, yes. However, if a policewoman performs some outstanding feat, the commissioner may appoint her a detective, with additional compensation. The only thing wrong with that is there's no security there. It's never a permanent appointment. It's at the commissioner's discretion— and any time he changes his mind, she's back to the base pay. Whereas any policeman who passes his civil service tests and is appointed to sergeant, lieutenant or captain can not be reduced in rank. Equality of the sexes doesn't exist in the police department!"

"Is there equality of risk involved?"

"A policewoman does not replace a patrolman," explained Mrs. Stewart. "She performs those jobs best performed by a

woman. But she takes plenty of chances." She pointed to the
chorus line. "See the third girl from the left?"

David looked toward a tall, attractive, blue-eyed brunette.
"That's Ethel Mackey. As soon as they finish rehearsing the
dance, I'll bring her over. She's been on the force five years.
For the past few months she's spent her nights walking through
lonely, dark streets in which women have been assaulted. She
loiters in bars, candy stores and restaurants where it's suspected narcotics are being sold. And she's frequently been assigned to skating rinks, the parks and other public places, to
pick up male offenders. Would you call that hazardous?"

"I certainly would," David admitted.

"She's not the only one—most of our young policewomen
are doing similar jobs."

"Who's that woman?" David nodded toward an elderly lady
sitting at the rehearsal table, studying a script. "Is she a policewoman's mother?"

Mrs. Stewart shot an amused glance at him, then called over
to the woman. "Florence! I want you to meet her anyway," she
explained. The lady raised her head, smiled and walked over.
"This is Mrs. Schuster, who is the nemesis of pickpockets."

David gulped. This grandmotherly soul went around trap-
ping pickpockets? His disbelief must have been apparent, for
Mrs. Schuster said, "I've got to be in court to testify tomorrow. We nabbed two old-time pickpockets in the subway today. Come by, if you like."

"I don't know if I can make it," demurred David. "Tell me,
how long have you been specializing in pickpockets?"

"Twenty years." Mrs. Schuster smiled at him. "I'm a grand-
mother, you know. And so is my partner. We've been working
as a team all that time."

"Where do you usually watch for them?"

"In crowds, of course," she replied. "Department stores, ele-
vators, subway trains. Oh," she looked toward the rehearsal

hub. "That's my cue. Good-bye, now!"

David turned to Mrs. Stewart. "She must be pretty success-ful. Who would ever expect a nice little old lady to be a cop? And with her partner—they must look like a pair of clucking matrons out for a day of shopping!"

Mrs. Stewart laughed. "That's the trick with all police-women—they never look like what they are, otherwise they'd be of no value."

The chorus line had disbanded and Mrs. Stewart beckoned the third girl from the left. Ethel Mackey came over—she was even better looking close up than at a distance—and begged off an interview.

"I'm due at the movies—I'm late already," she explained.

"A date?" asked David.

"No—my job," explained the girl.

David put his notebook away. "Would you mind if 1 went with you?" he asked. "I've got to be back at the office soon, anyway." As the girl hesitated, he added, "I won't be in your way. As a matter of fact, I can't stay long. I just want to see what you do."

She smiled in sudden agreement. "All right. I'll be dressed in a jiffy. See you in front of the building in five minutes." She scurried toward a room in the back which they had appropri-ated as a dressing room.

David thanked Mrs. Stewart for her help, and she gave him a few typewritten sheets of paper containing a brief history of women in the police department.

On his way out, David stopped by Wesley Foote's office and filled him in. "I probably won't do anything special with this —not right now, anyway. But it's good background informa-tion which I know will come in handy in the future."

"It sure will," agreed Foote. "One day you'll have a story in which policewomen will figure prominently—and oh, how thankful you'll be then!"

In the lobby of the building, David spotted Ethel Mackey as she emerged from another elevator. She wore an attractive suit and high heels and looked like one of the many pretty young secretaries who worked in the adjoining skyscrapers.

Miss Mackey explained she was "working" the Broadway houses, and, in the subway en route uptown, she told David what she watched for in a movie house.

Of the mashers, she said: "They're easy to spot. You see a woman move away from a man, and you see the man move up close to her again or to another woman—that's a man you watch. The hard part is to get a woman who's been annoyed to press charges. She doesn't want publicity.

"Then there are the seat-tippers," she continued. "They always sit behind the empty seat on which a woman lays her purse. Then they gently tilt that seat with their foot until they can reach through and pull the purse into their hands. They work awfully fast."

"When you aren't after mashers and pickpockets—what does a policewoman do?" David asked.

Ethel smiled. "A little of everything. My friend Jane Stevens was just promoted to detective. She was working with two men detectives on a narcotics case, and they were arresting two men who had just sold her some heroin. She'd made contact with these pushers before, and now they drove up to the corner where she was waiting and sold her a large amount. Anyway, as soon as they handed her the dope, the detectives rushed them and the pushers began to put up a fight. Janey jumped to the getaway car and clung to the window. She shot one man in the leg and knocked out the driver with the butt of her gun."

David was plainly impressed. "Your friend Janey must be quite a girl. I don't think I would care for a job as a decoy."

As the train pulled into the Times Square station, the two

emerged into the late afternoon sunshine.

"Do many people go to the movies at this hour?" asked David. It was four p.m.

"By the thousands," Ethel Mackey assured him.

"Which one are we going to?" David asked.

She motioned toward one of the big cinema houses.

David looked at the title on the marquee. "That one got excellent reviews," he told her as they walked toward the box office.

"Did it?" Ethel was surprised. "I'll have to come in and see it when I'm off duty."

"Can't you watch the picture while you're working?"

"Oh, my no! I never look at the screen. I've been in here a half dozen times since this film opened and I know the dialogue fairly well, but I've never seen the picture. Look," she turned to him. "I'm going to keep moving around in there, so please don't feel you have to observe the amenities. We can say good-bye right here, and you leave whenever you want to. It's pretty dull, anyway, just watching me watch!"

David bought two tickets at the box office, after which she addressed her final words to him. "That was a real waste of money," she said reprovingly. "I don't have to pay to get in here—my Police Department badge gets me in. I'm here to protect their customers, and they're happy to have me!"

"I didn't know," whispered David, for they were now in the theater. "But don't worry—I won't pay for it either. I'll put it on my expense account!"

"Fine! Bye now." David could scarcely hear her, for she had moved off to the side. For a few seconds, as the screen darkened, he couldn't see her, either. Then, as the action on the screen lightened, he caught sight of her over at the side, behind the last row of seats, in the orchestra. As she stood there, ostensibly watching the silver screen, her keen blue eyes were shifting like those of a combat pilot deep in enemy territory. After a while, she moved over to the other side of the theater, alert and watchful. . . . A little later, when she walked to the stairs leading to the balcony, David left the theater and headed back for the *Ledger* office.

He knew he would have to readjust his thinking on the "weaker" sex.

☆☆☆ 27

OUT-OF-TOWN ASSIGNMENT

DAVID HAD FREQUENTLY WONDERED about the mechanics of an out-of-town assignment, and then, quite unexpectedly, he found himself in the midst of one.

A big vice story had broken in Paxton, a large city in a nearby state. The story had interesting ramifications. It hinted at many things: big society and political wheels were involved (but not named), and the manipulators of the vice ring reportedly had headquarters in three states, including New York. It was this last item which interested Holloway.

"Go up to Paxton tomorrow and check on the New York angle," he told David. "Let's see if there's anything to it or if Paxton just can't bear to have a vice scandal all to itself."

David went back to his desk and put in a call to the district attorney of Paxton. He was agreeably surprised at the rapidity with which the call went through—no secretaries, no waits, no announcements. Public figures outside New York, David was to learn, were amazingly accessible. David mentioned the purpose of his call, said he hoped to be in Paxton the next day and would appreciate it if the d.a. would grant him an interview.

"Any time at all," replied the prosecutor affably.

"Two p.m.?" David queried.

"Two p.m. is fine with me," boomed the d.a. "I'll expect you then."

That done, David checked the *Ledger's* news service, to see which paper in Paxton was a subscriber. The *Ledger* had a number of special features which it syndicated to newspapers throughout the country. Thus, there was a special sort of rapport between the *Ledger* in New York and over a hundred papers in cities throughout the country. The news service editor told David the Paxton *Clarion* was his paper.

After that, David checked the railroad terminal for the schedule. He decided to take the 8:20 a.m. train, which would get him into Paxton about eleven.

A call to the district attorney's office in New York evinced the information that the local officials had very little on the scandal. "We're waiting word from Paxton," an assistant d.a. told David. "As soon as they give us what they have, we'll check our end."

David spent the next hour closely perusing the wire service stories on the scandal and jotting down all pertinent data.

Shortly after eleven the following morning, David presented himself to the day city editor of the Paxton *Clarion*. The *Clarion* office was a short walk from the railroad terminal, and David found it easily.

After introducing himself, he stated the purpose of his visit and he was agreeably impressed with the spirit of camaraderie which this stirred up. "Surest thing you know," the editor said, "we'll be glad to help you out."

Beckoning a reporter over to the city desk, he made quick work of the introductions. "Tim, this is David White of the

New York *Ledger.* David has come up to look into the vice story." Turning to David, he continued, "This is Tim Hudson. Tim's been covering the story for us and knows every facet of it. He'll be glad to fill you in."

Tim guided David toward the *Clarion's* morgue and requisitioned the necessary clips. "Look through these, and I'll be back in a little while to give you details."

David spent a half hour pouring through the clips and then looked about for Hudson. Almost immediately, the *Clarion* man caught his eye and walked over. "All through?" he asked. David nodded and then the two reporters began discussing the case in detail.

When David mentioned he had a two-o'clock appointment with the district attorney, Tim gave him some background for the meeting. "The d.a. is very ambitious—a great joiner, belongs to all the fraternal and social organizations. Among the big shots rumored to be connected with the vice ring are a number of Paxton's sacred elephants—the pillars of our society." Tim smiled. "And since our district attorney wants to become a judge, he obviously doesn't want any enemies —particularly not in high places."

David whistled. "Very interesting," he commented.

"Let's go have some lunch," suggested Tim, "and we can continue this fascinating discussion."

The two young reporters went around the corner to a small restaurant, obviously a favorite with *Clarion* personnel, and continued the discussion of Paxton politics and intrigue. David learned, to his amazement, that in Paxton it was perfectly legal for the district attorney to maintain a private legal practice. Some of the suspected town worthies were likewise suspected of being the d.a.'s personal clients, which added to the mess. So far as Tim knew, however, this was purely a Paxton scandal —he knew of no New York angle worth mentioning. "Oh, one or two New Yorkers may have attended some of the parties—

but I don't think we imported any talent." Tim grinned. "We
have enough of our own right here."

David looked at his watch and discovered, to his surprise,
that his appointment with the d.a. was only fifteen minutes
off. "I don't even know where his office is," he told Hudson,
as they paid their checks.

"Be my guest," Tim replied. "I'm headed for there, too."

They took a taxi for the mile-and-a-half trip, and David
noticed with interest that Paxton's taxi fare was computed by
zone, as compared with New York, where the fare was
computed by distance and the time consumed en route. David
tried to figure the cost of a ride this length in a New York
taxi, but gave up the effort in short order . . . there were just
too many obstacles to such computation. A couple of street
excavations or a row of buses and you'd miss three lights and
the meter would go skyrocketing. A ten-block cab ride in
Manhattan once cost him $1.80, David remembered wryly—
the cab got stuck in heavy crosstown traffic.

Finally, the cab pulled up before a fairly modern building,
and the two reporters stepped out.

Tim directed David through a series of hallways and then
to a self-service elevator, which finally brought them to their
destination. Hudson knew the reception clerk well and told
him that David White, of the New York *Ledger,* had an appointment with the d.a.

The clerk telephoned inside and within twenty seconds
David could hear a voice at the other end of the connection
say, "Send him in."

"I'll wait here," Tim said. "I'm sure he doesn't want to
see me. Besides, I can catch him later."

Despite the fact that he was armed with inside information,
David was nevertheless surprised at the easy charm of the
district attorney. He was smiling, affable and ingenuous. De-
ploring the newspaper stories, he pooh-poohed their contents.

"Nothing much to it," he told David seriously. "You know—a good story sells newspapers, so the natural tendency is to build a mediocre story up to the level of a good one."

"You think the Paxton newspapers are overplaying the story?" queried David.

"Of course. After all, if there was something to this, wouldn't my investigators have brought it out?" he asked.

"Haven't they?" parried the reporter.

"Not a bit of it," returned the district attorney stoutly. Then he asked David about a number of city officials whom the prosecutor knew in New York.

Finally, David returned once again to the investigation of the morals ring, and once again the d.a. belittled the story. "This conspiracy is not nearly as large as some people seem to think," he said petulantly. "There may have been one or two instances where New York was involved, but on an extremely small scale. Until we have the evidence, however, it would be most unethical for me to disclose the identity of those involved," he concluded.

When the interview was terminated, David noted with surprise that the prosecutor had given him more than an hour of his time—something that the district attorney in New York would rarely do.

"We like to treat our visitors from New York well," the Paxton prosecutor said, shaking hands with his visitor in farewell.

Outside, Hudson was waiting for David, and they returned to the *Clarion* office together. From the bits of information he had obtained from the district attorney, and the larger amount he had obtained from Tim Hudson and the *Clarion* clippings, David felt he had a semblance of a story.

Back in the *Clarion* city room, David noticed for the first time that it was less than half the size of the *Ledger's*. The *Clarion* was also a morning paper and things were now beginning to pick up there. Its rewrite bank, David noticed, consisted of three men, where the *Ledger* at that hour would have six.

Hudson showed David to a typewriter which was not in use—one quite similar to the machine that David used in his own office. But before writing, he called the *Ledger*—reversing the charges—and got Holloway. David told the city editor what he had, and that the lead was that the Paxton district attorney, without naming names, said that some New Yorkers were involved.

"Give me about two-thirds of a column and use the telephone recording, Dave," Holloway said.

David wrote his story and again called the *Ledger* collect. This time, he called the telephone recording office directly and got Bertha, a crackerjack, he was to find, at working a recording machine.

"Bertha," David said, "how does this thing work? What do I do?"

"You just speak clearly and distinctly—and as fast as you like. Don't worry about speed. I'm hooking you up to a recording machine which will catch everything you say. Only one thing—when you mention any names, be sure to spell them out and when you come to the end of a sentence, say 'period' and when you want a new paragraph, say so. Also, when you're quoting, be sure to say 'quotes.' That's about all. I'll listen in as you're talking and, if anything doesn't sound quite clear to me, I'll cut in and ask you about it. When you're all finished, tell me, and then I'll use an electric typewriter and take the story off the record. It's as simple as that. I'll have your copy on the city desk within fifteen minutes after you finish dictating."

"Do you throw the record away when you're finished?"

"Oh, no."

"I've never heard my own voice."

"Well, when you get back, come up here and listen to your heart's content!"

David then began to read the copy he had just written, and within eight minutes he was all through. However, before signing off, he had Bertha switch him back to the city desk, where he told one of the assistants that he had finished filing his story and that he was heading back for New York on the next train, which was leaving in thirty minutes.

David sought out the Paxton city editor and Hudson and thanked them for their extreme courtesy.

"Any time," they said cordially. "We like to help visiting firemen."

"Well, whenever you're in New York, be sure to drop in at the *Ledger* and maybe I can be of some service."

"Will do," they replied.

☆☆☆ *28*

SIEGE IN UPPER MANHATTAN

ALICE AND DAVID had just finished an early lunch in the outdoor cafeteria at Central Park. It was a cool Sunday in early March, and the wintry sun felt good. The sea lions were taking a midday siesta on the concrete ledges of the pool when the young couple walked past, heading toward the Fifth Avenue exit. As Alice pulled her gloves on, she grimaced in pain.

"What's the matter?" asked David.

"My darn ring!" she replied. "My father gave it to me as a

high-school graduation present, and I've never had it off my finger. It started to feel tight lately, and last night I tried to get it off. I pulled and yanked and used soap and oil and what not. It wouldn't budge and now my finger feels as though it's encased in a tight band of steel."

"A jeweler could take it off," David told her.

"Fine!" retorted Alice. "Don't you think I thought of that? You find me a jeweler and I'll be delighted. It's Sunday, remember?"

"Does it hurt much?" David asked solicitously.

"Quite a bit," she admitted. "I'd have been better off if I'd left it alone. But all that pulling last night didn't help any." She slipped her glove off. On the fourth finger of her left hand was a small gold ring with the initials "A.R." interwoven in script, and a small diamond chip next to it. The skin immediately surrounding the ring was puffed and blue-looking.

"I don't like the way that looks at all," said David apprehensively. "To heck with waiting till tomorrow for a jeweler to open. Let's walk over to the precinct. Somebody there will know what to do."

"Oh, no!" Alice stopped short. "I'm not going to annoy the police with my silly problem. I'd feel foolish!"

David took her elbow and walked purposefully onward. "I'd rather you felt foolish than lose a finger. Besides, there's no reason to feel foolish. All we're going to do is ask. If they can help, fine. If not, we'll look elsewhere. Come on!"

Somewhat reluctantly, Alice permitted herself to be led. The aching finger was throbbing painfully and pretty soon they were striding along in step.

"It's my own fault," she told him. "I'm probably getting fat."

David looked at her and laughed. "The only place you're getting fat is around the head—for not taking it off long ago," he chided her affectionately.

After walking about fifteen minutes, they turned into the block which David knew so well. He pointed out the old brownstone building with the flag jutting out and soon he led her up the familiar steps.

"I've never been in a police station in my life," Alice whispered.

"There always has to be a first time," he told her as they entered the high-ceilinged room. To the right, just in front of the wooden railing, sat Lieutenant McCarthy. He and David greeted each other warmly. David introduced Alice and explained the reason for the visit.

"The 'Boy Scouts' can handle that," the lieutenant told them. "They take on all such jobs. That's the Emergency Service Division," he added in fuller explanation. "They have a station just six blocks west of here, and all the equipment is there. You ever been there?"

"No," David admitted. "I've seen them in action, though— mostly, of course, applying oxygen."

"They do a good deal more," the lieutenant advised him. "They jack up subway trains when somebody falls underneath one, and they take care of almost every other emergency you can imagine—from a fat lady stuck in a bathtub to a building collapse. That's quite a setup," he added with admiration.

"Well, we'll find out whether they can take a tight ring off a lady's hand," David said, steering Alice toward the door. "Thanks for the suggestion, Lieutenant."

"Think nothing of it. I'm sure they'll fix you up fine," the lieutenant told them in parting.

As they walked along, David said teasingly, "Well, now you've been in a police station. Imagine living all your life here in New York and never seeing the inside of a police station!"

"I know," Alice replied with mock meekness. "It's because I've lived such a sheltered life. Imagine—I've never dated a murderer or even a paltry embezzler!"

After a while they approached what appeared to be a loft building, with a ramp leading into a garage. A number of men in blue coveralls were placing various items into a large Emergency Service Division truck and into two smaller station-wagon type cars.

"Those are the Emergency Service Police," David told Alice. "The blue coveralls are their uniform."

As the two young people walked into the building, they were met by a lieutenant. David proferred his press card and explained the reason for the visit. Alice, viewing the activity of the men, was very apologetic.

"I'm terribly sorry," she told the lieutenant. "If it's any imposition, please don't bother. I'm sure my finger will hold up until tomorrow!"

The lieutenant eyed the puffy finger and smiled. "No trouble at all. We'll have it off in a second. Smitty!" he called. One of the blue coveralled men came over. "A ring job," explained the lieutenant, indicating Alice. The man nodded and walked off. In a few seconds he was back with a small piece of metal in his hand. He directed Alice to a chair near the desk. "Sit down."

As Alice extended her hand apprehensively, Smitty smiled.

"Don't worry," he told her. "We've done an average of one a day for the past twenty years. Never lost a patient yet—or a finger!"

Alice was surprised. "You mean you cut rings off regularly?"

"Regular as clockwork," she was assured. "I'll even tell you what happened—the ring's been annoying you for some time and yesterday or this morning you started fooling with it and it wouldn't come off. Right?" She nodded. "And from the looks of it," he continued, fitting a thin piece of metal between her swollen finger and the ring, "you tried real hard!" The finger throbbed so, it was a real effort for Alice to hold it still.

Smitty noticed it and soothed her. "This will only take a minute and it won't hurt. Relax now."

As David and the lieutenant stood over her, watching the operation, Smitty took a tiny circular saw, the size of a five cent piece, and hooked it under the ring. It was made of highly tempered steel, with fine serrated teeth. Attached to it was a wing nut, and as he turned the nut, the teeth of the small saw cut into the ring. It took no more than ten turns and the ring was cut through. Everyone sighed with relief.

Alice gently massaged her hand. "I can't tell you how grateful I am—it was almost worse than a toothache!" She dropped the broken ring into her handbag. "Let's go, David. We're keeping these good people from their work."

"Wait a second." David turned to the lieutenant. "I thought the Emergency Service men were the lifesavers of the police force. What's that the men are putting into the truck?"

The lieutenant glanced over. "Those are riot guns. You're wrong—while we carry lots of lifesaving equipment, we also carry firearms—rifles, tear gas, grenades and metal vests, among other things. The word 'emergency' means just that—it can be an emergency for the police, too, you know. You get a couple of mean killers holed up in a house and we move on that, right along with the rest, maybe even faster. We try to smoke them out with tear gas and then we put the metal vests on the men who are going in after them." He grinned at the look of surprise on David's face. "Why—did you picture us only as male Florence Nightingales?"

David made a quick recovery. "Well, if I did—I don't anymore." He laughed. "Thanks for everything, Lieutenant."

Although he didn't know it at the time, David was to see the Emergency Service Division in full action, exactly as described, before the day was over.

As they walked out into the street, David asked, "Alice, would you mind if we dropped up to the office for a minute?

I want to see if there's anything new on Dawson."

Frank Dawson was a professional killer who was on the loose in upper Manhattan. He was wanted for a murder, and a few days ago, acting on information, the police had found him in a woman's flat. They searched him cursorily and then, as they were about to lead him out, Dawson turned on the patrolmen with a pistol in his hand. He disarmed them and escaped. Later that afternoon, a detective went looking for him. Dawson ambushed him in the hall of a building and took two wild shots at him before plunging down the stairs to escape a second time.

Apart from the fact that Dawson was a mean thug who would butcher anyone who stood in his way, the reputation of the police department was at stake. On a more or less routine arrest, he had not only escaped but had filched the guns of his would-be-captors. And on their second try, he had almost killed a detective.

David knew that the police had enlisted every known source of information. It was now only a matter of time before a tip came through. In the meanwhile, this tough killer with nothing to lose was holed up somewhere with plenty of artillery. The whole city was edgy with suspense.

Almost as soon as he and Alice walked into the city room, David knew something was up. Jim Bryan was on the desk and he called David over as soon as he spotted him.

"Dave! They got Dawson. That is—they haven't got him yet—he's holed up in an apartment uptown and they're shooting it out. The bulletin just came in. Tom Martin and Steve Blake have already gone out; you go out, too. Mulvaney will write the lead story—call in with what you've got. When you get back, you can do a side story." He wrote the address on a slip of paper.

David took the paper and ran. He was halfway to the elevator when he remembered something and turned back.

"Alice?" She was smiling indulgently at him from the far end of the room. "You understand, don't you?"

She waved him on. "Have fun. I'll see you tomorrow."

The elevator doors opened and David darted in.

Within a few minutes, he was in a subway car, headed uptown toward the scene of the mass siege.

As David emerged from the subway, he tucked his press card in his hat and walked along the curb. It was virtually impossible to walk on the streets—they were jammed with thousands of curious onlookers. As he glanced upwards, he noticed heads sticking out of all windows. He decided to get up on a nearby roof, if he could.

A lieutenant on duty filled him in. An hour previously, two detectives and their men had groped their way down a dark hallway to the door of the rear flat in which Dawson was entrenched. They knocked. There was no response. They turned the knob and pushed. The door swung open and there was a burst of gunfire. Dawson was crouching in the far doorway, shooting as fast as the hammer would fall. The two detectives fell and their companions dragged them back into the hall as the door panels split under the impact of more bullets from inside.

More police were called, including four emergency squads. In all, there were about two hundred policemen there. The six-story tenement was emptied of most of its tenants. Police were posted in a lot in the rear of the house, and in facing windows of houses alongside the building. Through these, they kept up a constant hail of bullets, interspersed with tear-gas bombs and grenades. All the roofs in the vicinity were filled with spectators or police.

It was a fantastic scene.

David ran around to the building across the courtyard from the one in which Dawson was entrenched. Since the criminal was in a fourth-floor apartment, David decided against posting himself on a roof and, instead, stopped after walking up three flights and headed for the apartment which would face the courtyard. As he ran through the door, he was greeted with, "Stay low and don't get in front of the window or you'll get your head blown off!" A patrolman was seated on the floor with his pistol in his right hand, resting on the window ledge, and his eyes at about the gun level. As David squatted down beside him, he fired a shot across the court. David stole a quick glance out the window. Dawson's fortress was ten yards away, across the courtyard. From somewhere else several more shots rang out.

"Duck!" yelled the patrolman. But neither knew whether the shots had been fired by Dawson or other officers in nearby apartments. When David commented on this, he was told, "Just duck—you can't see a bullet, and anybody's bullet can kill you just as fast."

In response to questions, between firing shells and reloading, David learned that the officer's name was William Stephens, that he was twenty-eight years old, had been on the police force three years, was married and had a youngster at home.

"I'm here because it's my duty," he said. "But what are you doing here?"

Amid the battle and above the staccato crossfire of bullets, they discussed the batting averages of current baseball players, outstanding foreign films and the peculiar charm of fishing in a quiet stream.

A roar from the throngs in the street reached their ears. "Those people," commented Patrolman Stephens. "They act like this was a circus or a ball game. Here we are, trying to kill Dawson, and he's trying to kill us, and they cheer!"

Other police officers shot tear gas into the apartment across the courtyard and in a moment flames and smoke were billowing out of the punctured windows. A new barrage of tear gas was poured into the window, but a freak backdraft forced it into the apartment where David and Patrolman Stephens were holing in. For a moment both of them had teary, burning eyes, and neither could see. It cleared up in a few seconds and they resumed their conversation. Patrolman Stephens reloaded his gun and started a fresh rain of bullets.

Meanwhile, firemen began pouring streams of water into the Dawson apartment and the flames gradually died out. Gunfire from the besieged windows seemed to have stopped. A police officer in plain clothes yelled, "Hold your fire—we're going in."

Patrolman Stephens checked his gun and said, "Now it comes. I hope one of our bullets got him."

After an interminable wait, a head was poked out the window. A detective shouted: "O.K., boys, we got him."

The patrolman and David got to their feet.

Officer Stephens extended his hand. "Look me up some time, Dave," he said. And David replied, "With pleasure, Bill. And we can swap stories about today."

A wintry twilight had set in when David emerged into the street. Tom Martin and Steve Blake were getting statistics on the spectacular siege from the Deputy Police Commissioner, who was on the scene, and David joined them. Afterward, they all headed for a phone and then came back to the *Ledger* office together.

Mulvaney wrote the main news story from material supplied by all three reporters, as well as the wire services. Tom Martin did a side story on a woman who had the apartment next door to Dawson and had misunderstood the police order to leave. She thought they were burglars banging on the door and spent the whole of the two-hour assault under her bed. Steve Blake wrote a piece on the amount of police equipment used, the number of men involved in the mass attack and the strategy which was employed. And David wrote a side story about chatting with a policeman in an apartment ten yards from the killer's windows, discussing life in general and sports in particular, as bullets whizzed by and an occasional whiff of tear gas left them with streaming eyes.

The most spectacular siege of the decade was well covered by the *Ledger* and, dangerous or not, David wouldn't have missed it for the world!

☆☆☆ *29*

WELFARE DEPARTMENT "SCANDAL"

ONE OF THE AFTERNOON NEWSPAPERS in town, the *Chronicle,* had been feuding with the city administration for some months. What precipitated the breach was uncertain, although many rumors flew. It was, however, fact and no rumor that the newspaper had been one of the mayor's staunchest backers during his campaign for election, only the year previously.

The *Chronicle* now harassed him from every angle. They concentrated on various civic ills, blew them up out of all proportion and somehow managed to fix the blame on the mayor. Though he had been in office not quite a year, they held him accountable for the city's slums. They also insisted, on the basis of a handful of employees, that morale in the police, fire and other city departments had hit a new low.

Then one day the paper blossomed out with an eight-column banner headline on page one: LADY IN MINK ON CITY RELIEF.

The subheadline read, "Mayor's Commissioner of Welfare Says He Will Correct Situation Immediately."

The story ran for more than a column and seemed well documented. The *Chronicle* gave the woman's name, address, age and background. While it gave no specific value for the fur coat, the word "mink" has only one popular connotation and the impression left with the readers was that this woman, in possession of a coat worth several thousand dollars, was nevertheless a recipient, on a regular monthly basis, of the the taxpayers' hard-earned money.

Within twenty-four hours, the story ripped the town wide open. Comedians on stage, TV and night clubs had only to mention the word "mink" and the audience burst into bitter cheers. City Hall was deluged with letters and phone calls, demanding a wholesale investigation.

Shortly after the story appeared, Holloway called David in.

"I know the *Chronicle* is out to embarrass the mayor and his administration and maybe they have something this time. And then again, maybe not." He handed David the original clipping on the lady in mink. "Go take a look," he told him.

David went around to the address listed in the story. It was a shabby neighborhood. He found the woman home in her apartment on the top floor of a five-story walk-up. With her were her two daughters, aged eight and six. The *Chronicle* had made no mention of any children.

David introduced himself and came right to the point.

"Do you have a mink coat?" he asked.

The woman burst into tears. "I certainly do," she wept, "and I want you to see it for yourself!" She walked into the next room and returned with a coat that, even to David's inexperienced eyes, looked as though it should have been discarded many years previously. It was a moth-eaten piece of junk, with a number of rips. Along the sleeves it was worn down to the skin. The woman eyed him fiercely and then spoke with elaborate sarcasm. "This is my fine mink coat! It cost a lot of money—two dollars at the church bazaar last year. It's such a fine-looking garment I'm ashamed to wear it out, so I use it to cover the children at night. We have no steam here, and I'm afraid to keep the kerosene burner going during the night." Her rage evaporated. She looked at David hopelessly and shrugged. "What's the use?" she said. "You won't believe me, either. When I went to the butcher and the grocer yesterday—they didn't believe me.

"When my girls went out to play, the neighbors stopped them and asked them questions. If I had money," she asked fiercely, "would I live like this?"

David looked around the apartment, which consisted of two rooms: the kitchen, which was also obviously the living room, and through the doorway, a small bedroom. The walls and ceiling were badly cracked, and the paint over the kitchen sink was peeling in large curls.

"What does your husband do?" asked David.

"He died three years ago. I worked for a year after he died, and I was able to manage until I developed bursitis. I had to quit. I went from one doctor to another, and my money ran out. I couldn't go back to work. You think I like living on charity? That reporter who wrote about the Lady in Mink— why didn't he come around to see me before he wrote such a story?" She smiled bitterly. "Maybe he was jealous. Maybe he wanted a mink coat for his wife. Tell him he can have this one, for the same price I paid. No—I'll give it to him free!"

David was convinced that the woman had told him the truth, but he had to check this out further. He went to see the Commissioner of Investigation, a middle-aged man who had been in social work for many years and was known for his integrity. In fact, he was considered such an efficient administrator that the city had hired him away from a midwestern community, where he had built up a national reputation.

En route to the commissioner's office, David bought another newspaper. This one, evidently also without doing any investigating, had picked the item up and also plastered the lady in mink story on page one.

"I guess that's the kind of story that sells newspapers," David mused.

He arrived at the office of the commissioner just as a mass press conference was beginning. On the commissioner's desk was the lady's file. She had been on relief, it showed, about two years.

"Gentlemen," the commissioner said, "I have not only questioned the woman, but also her case worker. This office has no apologies and no explanations whatsoever. This woman is entitled to the relief she is getting, despite the headlines and stories in some papers. I might say at this point that one newspaper inaccurately quotes me as saying that I 'will correct the situation immediately.' I not only never said that—I never had the opportunity to say anything. That newspaper never even gave me the courtesy of calling me to get this department's view on the case!"

The *Chronicle* reporter present at the press conference spoke up. "I had nothing to do with that story," he said. "I'm only doing leg work on this, and was sent over to cover this conference."

Another reporter questioned, "O.K., Commissioner, what about those other cases—where families on relief are supposedly living the life of royalty in hotels, with all expenses paid by the city?"

"I'm glad you brought that up," the commissioner snapped. "There are exactly seventeen families on relief living in hotels. I question your characterization of their living like royalty. These seventeen families lived in a tenement which was completely burned out four days ago. In order to keep the families together, we have put them up at a hotel where the cost is extremely moderate. They will probably stay there another day or two, by which time we feel we will have found other lodging for them. We have no recourse other than the hotel, without splitting up the family—the father to the men's shelter, the mother to the women's shelter, and the children to the children's shelter. A number of the children are under five years of age, which would make this an extremely heartless, as well as impracticable act. A family which has been burned out has suffered enough, without adding to their misery."

As David walked into the *Ledger* city room, Holly beckoned him over. A late edition of the *Chronicle* was spread across his desk, headlining the story of relief recipients living in hotels.

"What's this about?" asked Holly.

"It's a slanted story and a mean piece of work," replied David spiritedly, and he told Holloway the facts about the Lady in Mink, as well as the "luxury hotels."

Holly heard him out and then said, "I half-expected it. Well, sit down and write it as you saw it. How did the commissioner strike you?"

"I never dealt with him before," replied David, "but I feel he's telling the truth and making the best of a bad situation." He looked at Holly reflectively. "What trouble you can create with half-truths!"

Holloway laughed. "That's how a lot of papers get sold."

"This story won't sell extra *Ledgers*," said David, "but it'll be accurate, and put things into their proper perspective, in spite of what the other newspapers might do."

"Fair enough." Holly turned back to his desk.

David's story brought in quite a few letters of commendation, including one from the governor's office. From the state capitol came word that, until the *Ledger* story appeared, the state's chief executive was contemplating an investigation into the city's welfare department, since state funds were involved in part.

"This is honest journalism," the governor wrote, "and I congratulate you for not being stampeded."

☆☆☆ *30*

DAVID RIDES IN A HELICOPTER

DAVID HAD NOT BEEN at Jackson Airport since the time of that airplane wreck, which gave him his first break in the newspaper field. Now he was there on a cold, windy, rain-swept morning—ready to take off in a helicopter.

The city desk had called him at home to tell him that the torrential rains of the last three days had just about wiped out every bridge in an adjoining state and whole towns were being flooded. Entire families were marooned on roof tops and the Coast Guard and the Navy were moving in to try to save all these stranded people. He was to cover their activities from a helicopter.

"Teddy Gleason will go along to take pictures. He'll meet you at the airport," David was told. "We've already arranged for the helicopter. There's one waiting for you. Better move fast—take-off time is in one hour."

David had been in an airplane a few times, but he had never been in an "egg beater." This should be exciting, he thought to himself. He was in the subway, on the way to Jackson Airport, within ten minutes after the office called.

Gleason, the photographer, was already at the hangar when David arrived, and David was glad to see him. Photographers, he had found out, were an unpredictable crew and some of them tended to get as temperamental as opera singers. At times, David thought ruefully, their talents didn't warrant the temperament. But Teddy was one of the exceptions. He was a round-faced, down-to-earth sort of guy who knew his business and no nonsense about it. He was unusually even-tempered and, thinking hard, David couldn't recall a single time that Teddy had ever gotten mad. Even now, on this miserable, wet, bone-chilling morning, Teddy's round face was wreathed in a smile as he said, "Hi, boy—we got California weather! I don't see how we can take off." He peered upwards into the rain-sodden clouds. "No ceiling at all."

The pilot, who was warming up his craft, stepped out of the machine and corroborated Gleason's statement, adding, "Maybe things will open up in the next half hour."

David, who had had the good sense to wear heavy old clothes, plus a windbreaker, shivered nevertheless. Then he realized he was hungry—he had jumped into his clothes without shaving and without eating. He noticed a vending machine and bought a large chocolate bar. It probably wasn't the ideal breakfast food, but since he couldn't spare the time to hike over to the airport's restaurant, it would have to do.

The three men stood there in the hangar, making desultory conversation until, about twenty-five minutes later, the torrent let up momentarily.

"Now's our chance—let's go," said the pilot, and the three of them hopped into the helicopter, which was a four-seater. The propellers made a tremendous roar and the craft went straight up!

"Hey, Teddy!" David laughed. "This is great. No long run before take-off. Zoom right up in the air!"

The machine levelled out at about eight hundred feet—for

the ceiling was no higher. It seemed to skid along. Down below, David could see familiar landmarks—the bridges and highways and the highly individual skyscrapers which he knew so well. A slight malaise came over him. "Teddy," he asked querulously, "does this thing have to buck so much?"

Gleason eyed him sharply. "For heaven's sake, Dave," he said apprehensively, "we aren't even there yet!"

"I don't know what you're talking about," returned David haughtily and resumed looking out the window. He had difficulty focusing, however. The small craft kept pitching and tossing, and a pained glaze covered his eyes. He closed them.

Within ten minutes, they were over the flood area in the adjoining state. David made a heroic effort and looked out the window. There was a man paddling a canoe in front of a row of one-family dwellings. Only three days ago, it had been a paved city street—and now it was a river. The water appeared to be on a level with the upper windows.

Suddenly, David felt very warm. He opened his windbreaker. He was still warm and the dismal feeling in the pit of his stomach intensified. He removed the windbreaker altogether and at this moment Gleason cheerily called to the pilot to release a switch so that he could open the compartment door to take a picture.

A gust of wet, icy air swirled around David's head, and he drooped lower in his seat in an attempt to avoid it. At this point, Gleason ordered the pilot, "Bank sharply to the right. I want to get a good shot of that man in the canoe."

The pilot obeyed swiftly, and David sank to the floor of the craft.

"Hey, Dave," Gleason called, his eye at the aperture of the camera, "don't you want to see this man waving up at us?"

David replied dully, "I can't . . ."

Gleason turned swiftly to look at his colleague. David's face was green. It was also quite obvious that the chocolate bar he had eaten a little while ago had not been the best choice for breakfast.

"Ah, well," said Teddy compassionately, "just take it easy, boy."

As the light craft continued to pitch its way through the air, Gleason snapped away with his camera. From time to time he issued instructions to the pilot and, in dutiful response, the little "egg beater" veered to the left and to the right. Every movement had its own distressing effect on the wretched reporter, who was lying prone on the floor. In his right hand he clutched his pencil. In his left was his notebook. He had not taken a single note—he was unable to.

After a while, the craft straightened out and headed straight up a river, which was overflowing at its banks for its entire length. Again, at Gleason's orders, the helicopter banked sharply this way and that. Once again the door was open for the ubiquitous camera. And David thought grimly that, if he had the strength, he'd just jump out and take his chances on where and how he would land—just as long as it remained steady.

Gleason was revoltingly cheerful. He jumped over David, from one side to the other, calling out what he was seeing.

"There's a Coast Guard duck taking on a load of people," Teddy shouted. "Hey, pilot—drop down lower and cut to the left." And the whirly-bird dropped with a lurch which found its echo in David's trembling insides.

The picture-taking continued for about twenty minutes. Then—at long last—Gleason told the pilot, "O.K., we can head back now."

This was the deliverance David had been waiting for. With a tremendous effort, he lifted himself off the floor of the craft and onto his seat. He reached for his windbreaker and put it around him—right now he was feeling very cold. The queasiness returned, and he rested his head between his legs.

After what seemed an eternity—but was in fact only twenty minutes—the helicopter was back at its take-off point. David shakily stepped out, assisted by Gleason and the pilot. After taking a half dozen steps on solid ground, he felt considerably better.

Gleason, who had driven out to the airport in a *Ledger* car, drove David back to the office. On the way, he filled the young reporter in on everything he had seen and snapped. Fortunately, Teddy was not only a good photographer, he was also a keen observer.

For all David had personally seen, he could have stood in bed.

"I'll have to fake it," he told Teddy. "Though I think you've given me enough to write three-quarters of a column."

They walked into the *Ledger* city room together. By then, the normal color had returned to David's face.

"Gosh, I'm glad to see you!" Holloway told David as he approached the desk. "We got a bulletin from American Press just about the time you were scheduled to take off. It said that an unidentified helicopter had made a forced landing, because of the weather, in Van Cortlandt Park. It gave no identification as to who was in it or whether anybody was hurt. We only just got word that it was a helicopter rented by the *Transcript*. Except for a bent propeller, it developed, no harm was done. But it kept the *Transcript* reporter and photographer from flying over the flood scene. You got a good story to write, Dave?"

"It will work out," answered David noncommittally and walked to his desk.

Gleason processed his pictures quickly and brought them over to David. The photographer gave David the location of each picture, as well as a word description of the general area surrounding the spot.

David wrote his story. He felt, in view of the fact that he had seen nothing except the floor of the helicopter, that he did a masterful job.

"The pictures were good, too," Holloway commented the next day.

It wasn't until a week later that David confessed the true happenings of the helicopter ride to his city editor.

Holloway roared with laughter. "Getting airsick is bad enough—but to have to write an eyewitness account immediately afterward—well, you've been punished enough. No point in my rubbing salt in the wound. Besides, it was a darn good story, all things considered!"

☆☆☆ *31*

THE WIRE-TAP CASE

FROM TIME TO TIME, David came up against cases in which wire tapping was involved. This was one of the knottiest problems in the courts—not only in New York, but around the country. Because of the intricate laws involved, what was illegal in federal courts was perfectly legal in state courts: a piece of evidence which almost literally put the noose around the defendant's neck in a state court could not even be hinted at in a federal court.

Therefore, with regard to wire tapping, a criminal reporter had to be as fully conversant with the hairsplitting laws as a top attorney—perhaps even more so. A lawyer had time to research the newest developments, or consult a specialist in the field. A reporter had, at most, only a few hours to digest the contents of a ruling and write a factual account for his newspaper.

It was after David had received a number of ponderous and contradictory opinions on the wire-tap laws that he realized that the situation had to be clarified for him. There were many reporters who took the easy way—they simply quoted excerpts from a court's opinion in their news stories and let it go at that. You never got into trouble that way, but it frequently happened that few readers could find their course in the foggy legal terminology. David, however, had an intelligent and curious mind. He was unhappy when he had to write about something he didn't fully grasp and so, after wading painstakingly through some recommended literature which did not clarify the issue for him, he telephoned to Judge Ezra Steiner.

Within an hour he was sitting in the now familiar presence of the spare little judge and had laid his problem before the sharp and analytical mind of the ex-jurist.

"Judge, I don't understand why there should be such a conflict of opinions about wire tapping. I don't understand why the wire-tap laws aren't consistent. In fact," he added slowly, "I don't understand why there should be wire tapping."

"You're not alone," replied Judge Steiner dryly.

"I feel," continued David, encouraged, "that wire tapping is a violation of our constitutional rights. The Fourth Amendment guarantees against 'unreasonable search and seizure,' and the Fifth Amendment safeguards individuals against self-incrimination. When somebody taps my telephone and listens to my conversations without my knowledge or my consent—that's a direct infringement of my rights!"

"The Supreme Court of the United States doesn't agree with you," said the judge quietly.

"They don't? Since when?" asked David incredulously.

"Since 1928, in what has since become famous as the Olmstead decision. You know," he interposed gently, "wire tapping is almost as old as the telephone itself—why, it was already used by the New York police away back in 1895. Public indignation was kind of slow, but gradually it grew. And finally, in the case of Olmstead, a bootlegger, defense attorneys succeeded in getting to the Supreme Court. They pleaded for a reversal of their client's conviction on the ground that wire tapping was used to gain evidence and that wire tapping violated the Fourth Amendment restriction on search and seizure —just as you so keenly observed."

"And what was their decision?"

"Their decision was the Olmstead decision, in which they ruled that the Fourth Amendment applied only to 'actual physical invasions' of privacy, and not to 'projected voices.' "

David was aghast. "But how could the men who wrote our Constitution conceivably foresee the inventions and wonders which were to come along in another century? Certainly the spirit of the law was violated!"

Judge Steiner smiled. "The Olmstead decision was a five-four decision. The four dissenters were Justices Brandeis, Holmes, Butler and Stone. The views of the four dissenters have carried as much weight in subsequent discussions as did the majority opinion. I assume you have heard the description of police wire tapping as 'dirty business'?"

"Yes, of course I have."

"Then you'll be interested to know that Justice Oliver Wendell Holmes was the author of it. And as for your comment on the spirit of the law rather than the letter of it," Judge Steiner smiled, "Justice Louis D. Brandeis argued that clauses of the Constitution guaranteeing to the individual protection against specific abuses of power should be adaptable to a changing world. He went further. He asked, 'Can it be that the Constitution affords no protection against such invasions of individual security?' But no one answered."

"Well, I'm relieved to find my opinions are shared by such brilliant men," said David. "But where does that leave us now?"

"In a mess." The judge laughed. "The people didn't take the Olmstead decision sitting down. There was considerable agitation for a statutory ban on wire tapping. And so Congress did it this way: when the Federal Communications Commission was established as an independent agency in 1934, they included in the enabling act, as Section 605, a provision which was intended to outlaw wire tapping once and for all." He paused and sighed.

"Why didn't it?" asked David.

"The way it was worded. It read in part, 'No person not being authorized by the sender shall intercept any communication and divulge or publish . . .' and so forth. Intercept and divulge. Do you see the fly in the ointment?"

David thought awhile. "It sounds precise enough to me . . . unless—do they mean it's O.K. to intercept, provided they don't divulge?"

"That's right," answered the judge. "That little word 'and' makes all the difference, since it means that both acts have to be committed before anything illegal has taken place."

"But nobody is going to tap a phone just for fun," expostulated David. "Anybody who does it is either going to divulge it or make some use of it!"

"They certainly are," agreed the judge, "but that's the situation."

"As of today?"

"Yes—as of today: in federal courts only, of course."

"How about the individual states?"

"The states make their own laws. In New York, for example, police officials are permitted to tap and the evidence thereby obtained is perfectly legal in state court."

David was plainly puzzled. "But how can something which is illegal in a federal court be legal in a state court?"

Judge Steiner was patient. "My boy, I have told you: the courts have different laws. Wire tapping is, in the present interpretation of the law, not a violation of your constitutional rights; it is merely a violation of a federal statute—providing the contents are divulged, of course. In fact, no evidence which stems from wire tapping is permissible in a federal court. Justice Frankfurter labelled it 'fruit of the poisonous tree.' "

David was thoughtful. "Judge," he said, "presumably a defendant can carry an appeal all the way to the Supreme Court, can't he?"

"Yes," replied the jurist, "provided, of course, that his contention is that his constitutional rights have been violated."

"Well," continued David, "supposing someone was convicted in New York on the basis of wire tapped information, and he pursued it up to the Supreme Court?"

"Someone did." Judge Steiner smiled. "The Stemmer case in 1948. I believe the man was convicted on a charge of bribing basketball players, and the information was obtained by the New York police by wire tapping. The case went all the way to the Supreme Court, and the verdict was four-four, with no opinion."

"Tied score," commented David. "What does that mean?"

"It means the conviction stands."

"Have there been other attempts to have the individual state laws termed unconstitutional?"

"Oh, yes. But none got any further."

David smiled at the judge. "These are merely attempts to get the narrow Olmstead decision off the books, aren't they?" he asked.

"Of course," replied the judge ruefully, "but so far, as you see, they've been unsuccessful."

David rose. "I'm very much indebted to you, Judge. While

I knew all the little pieces of the laws, I was never too clear on how they fit together. I must say, though, that this is quite a mess."

Judge Steiner laughed aloud and offered his hand in farewell. "I must say," he mimicked David's thoughtful tone, "that I thoroughly agree with you!"

A week following his illuminating conversation with the judge, David found himself handling one of the biggest wiretap scandals of recent years. And before the trial was over, he fully appreciated Justice Holmes' remark that wire tapping was a "dirty business."

In New York State, law officers are permitted to wire-tap on court orders. In addition, however, civilians were permitted to tap their own phones. A businessman, for instance, who suspected his employees of transmitting confidential business matters to a competitor could hire a professional eavesdropper to record all telephone conversations from his place of business. Or a man seeking evidence for a divorce could order his home phone tapped.* But these questionably legitimate motives were frequently a smokescreen for blackmail and avarice, as was all too evident at the trial of Peter Hawkes, expert wire tapper.

Police had raided a plush apartment on the swank east side, where they found extensive wire-tap equipment being operated by two men. This illegal wire-tap operation was so vast, the electronic equipment so elaborate, it was capable of tapping more than 100,000 phones—in the wealthiest area of the city. It looked like a Hawkes setup, and the police set about proving it.

Peter Hawkes was a lawyer who had been arrested several times in recent years on wire-tap charges—but he always managed to beat them. He had been unsuccessful during his years

---

* In 1957, the N.Y. State Legislature passed a law which forbids civilian wiretapping under any circumstances.

at the bar and, having an excellent mechanical bent and an ambition for financial success, he deserted his law offices for the shady but profitable business of wire tapping. He was one of the biggest operators in the field and, while it was well known that he did not limit himself to the legitimate phases of it, to date nothing had been proved.

All that was due to change, however, with the arrest of the two men in the east side "nest."

As soon as Hawkes' name entered the investigation, David telephoned him. Hawkes admitted that he was a wire tapper, but insisted he was a legitimate one.

It soon developed that the two men found in the apartment turned state's evidence—that is, they admitted their part in the conspiracy and testified against the head of the ring, their boss, Hawkes.

At his trial, Hawkes repeated what he had told David: that he tapped phones, but only the phone of a subscriber who hired him. But the district attorney's office showed that this was not quite the whole truth. Hawkes, for instance, when hired by a cosmetic concern with a new product, not only tapped that firm's own phones, but also tapped the phones of its competitors. (The evils inherent in the power of eavesdropping were made more forceful when it became apparent that the original cosmetic firm had paid for these additional taps.)

There was a parade of outraged witnesses to the court: actresses, models, businessmen, corporation directors. All took the stand to testify that they had never hired Hawkes to listen in on their phones. The fact was that he had been hired by somebody else, who was interested in blackmail or personal gain.

One irate art dealer testified that the unauthorized tap had caused him to suffer severe business losses. He explained that, whenever an art dealer gets wind of a particularly desirable acquisition, the idea is to keep it quiet and buy it before the price is jacked up. This man had not realized until now why he had been unable to make a single good purchase in months —a competitor had put a tap on his phone, and bought every worth-while thing first.

A handsome, middle-aged society woman took the stand. She had been estranged from her husband, but at the present time they were back together again. During the period of their separation, she had received a telephone call from Mr. Hawkes, asking her to come down to his office.

When she got there, Mr. Hawkes mentioned the name of a prominent actress who was frequently seen in the company of her husband. The lady said she was aware of the situation. Hawkes then played off some recorded telephone conversations between the husband and the actress. He asked the woman whether she wouldn't like to hear all of them and mentioned a weekly fee. The wife said she felt there was nothing to be gained by this and refused.

There was so much of this that David could only question the wisdom of the five Supreme Court justices who held that wire tapping was not unconstitutional. Along with Justice Brandeis, he thought, "can it be that the Constitution affords no protection against such invasions of individual security?"

Peter Hawkes was convicted on seventeen wire-tap counts.

But the Hawkeses are an indomitable lot, mused David. You crush one and fifty spring up in his place. Wire tapping is just too easy, too available and the opportunities for wealth and blackmail are apparently too irresistible. This one, thought David, is right up the alley for the Supreme Court—if only they'd stop ducking.*

* In December, 1957, the Supreme Court took a big step in the direction of outlawing wire taps. In a unanimous decision, the court set aside a conviction (in an alcohol tax case) on the grounds that the wire tap evidence, although legally obtained by state law, was illegal and inadmissible in a federal court. Many lawyers interpret this as making all wire taps inadmissible in any court. Obviously, the legal boundaries of this step, called the Benanti Decision, have yet to be explored.

MORE DETECTIVE STORIES

"WERE YOUR EARS burning last night?" David asked Terry Mulligan. Not having seen the jaunty detective in some time, he had called him and the two men were now relaxing over a cup of coffee in a cafeteria near the east side precinct.

"Why should my ears burn?" the detective asked. "Were you giving me a raking over?"

"No, you lug," replied David. "I was telling a friend of mine that you were probably having a busy night. It was a full moon," he added.

"Blonde or brunette?"

"Blonde—if that makes a difference," said David impatiently.

"Boy—you're out with a blonde and there's a full moon and you talk about me? I must really rate!"

Under David's reproachful look, the detective relented.

"Davey," he sighed, "we don't need a full moon to keep us busy. This is one business that knows no slack season. The nuts keep us busy 365 days a year."

"Anything special now?" queried the reporter.

"Now—yesterday—tomorrow—always. You know the Wagner murder last week—that shady financier who was found shot in his fancy mansion on Fifth Avenue? Well, the jerks are back at it—six confessions to date and twenty-three hot tips. Tips!" he added in disgust.

"And nothing came from the batch?" asked David.

"I didn't expect anything but a headache—and I got that," replied Terry wearily.

David was thoughtful. "I knew there were always a few psychotics who came along with phoney confessions and tips but I didn't know there were that many."

"This is only the beginning," replied Mulligan earnestly. "Mark my words, that number will be tripled, at least, before the month is out. And if we don't break the case by then, every time there's a mention of it in the papers—a new batch of lamebrains will come to life."

David straightened in his chair. "Does this happen with every murder?" he asked.

"With those which are well publicized, yes. And the worst part of it is that we can't afford to pass anything by—there's always the slight chance there may be something to it."

"Wait a minute," interrupted David. "Are you talking about people who deliberately call up with misinformation as a sort of practical joke—or those who think something they know might be of value?"

"The sincere citizens aren't too bad—and not too numerous—although I'll get back to them later. I'm talking about the boys who have one too many at the corner bar and suddenly decide it would be a hilarious joke if they called the precinct and told the cops they'll find the Wagner murderer at such and such night club. Or those other boys who have a yen to see their pictures in the papers, so they walk into the station house and say, 'I'm your man. I shot him.' "

"How do you know one of them isn't telling the truth?" asked David curiously. "Is it so unlikely that a man's conscience could make him come out and give himself up?"

Terry laughed. "Davey—when you've seen as many of these guys as we have, you know they're a little sick mentally. In the first place, just so's you'll understand—we weren't born yesterday. The information and the clues we give to the press isn't by any means the whole story. We always leave out a couple of things we're working on—and they're pretty vital things. So when a character walks in and rattles off the story already in the *Ledger* or the *Transcript,* we waltz him right out again. He needs a hospital, not a police station."

"How about the callers?"

Terry muttered violently. "I'd like to put every one of them behind bars! The man power that's wasted checking those phoney tips!" He paused. "But a little while ago you mentioned the honest people of the city who telephone in good faith. What's good faith mean, anyway? I've begun to doubt there is any such thing. You remember the Bomb Maniac?" he asked.

The Bomb Maniac was an appellation pinned on the unknown person who, for some years, had been placing homemade bombs in public places about the city. In the many years of the maniac's activity, his actions were given scant attention in the press, by request of the Police Department. They felt that a great amount of publicity would only spur the maniac on to further activity and would, moreover, give rise to a number of would-be imitators. However, as he got more daring, the Department finally relaxed the ban and went completely the other way in an all-out hunt which led to his eventual capture.

David smiled. "Sure I remember the maniac—he hogged the front page for quite a while."

Terry eyed his companion wryly. "We got him just about in time. Another week or two and we wouldn't have had any men available—they'd all be out checking phoney tips. But tips," his voice was laden with sarcasm, "supplied by solid citizens acting in good faith, just like you said!"

David knew what was coming and smiled. He had written the side story to the capture, covering just that aspect of the police work.

"You know I don't have a very high regard for human nature," Terry said evenly, "but I always thought that was because the kind of human nature I usually run into is sub-level. But here you had solid citizens, who had lived next door to their neighbors for five, ten, twelve years, catching the hysteria and calling the cops—by the hundreds, mind you!—to turn in their own neighbors and friends. Every guy who had a little power saw or a small machine shop in his basement got reported as the maniac by his good friends next door. It was like during the war," Mulligan interrupted himself morosely. "There was a kid on my block had a punctured eardrum. He got called down to the draft board for a physical regularly because every time one of his friends got drafted, the friend's mother wrote a letter to the board, asking why this kid wasn't in—and suggesting there was something shady about it. They made the poor kid's life so miserable the family had to move away. And the kid would have given his eyeteeth to get into the service!"

"That was a pretty disgraceful exhibition, I know," soothed David, "but your hunt for the maniac must have had a couple of laughs in it once or twice? Yes?"

Terry thought a while, and then laughed aloud. "Yep—I remember one guy in particular. You know, the maniac always left his souvenirs in public places. So we always had a couple of guys checking the terminals and some of the big department stores. One day we get a tip that a suspicious guy is hanging around Lorcy's department store. The store had already had two real bombs planted there, but, fortunately, they were discovered before they went off, so I went after that one myself. Anyway, I tailed this guy for about a week; he had an almost rigid routine. Every day about noon he came into the store carrying a brief case. He made straight for a telephone booth located in an obscure corner in the basement, and sat in the booth for almost a half hour, with the door closed. I could see he was not using the phone. When he'd come out, I'd examine the booth, to see if he'd planted anything there. Nothing. He would then leave the store and go to an office building across the street. At 5:15, he left the office building, and I followed him home—and once he got home, he never left his house until the following morning, when he went back to the office building. At noon, he was back in Lorcy's, in the same phone booth. I made some inquiries and learned he was an accountant with a company in the office building where he spent most of the day."

"What was he doing in the phone booth?"

"That's what I wanted to know. I had established that he had nothing at home with which to make bombs. Anyway, as he came out of the phone booth after about a week of my tailing him, I brought him into the precinct for questioning. He was quite agitated when I brought him in. I asked him to open that brief case." Mulligan paused and smiled.

"Well, what was in it?" pressed David.

Mulligan burst out laughing. "Egg shells, the remains of an apple, a mess of crumbs and an empty coffee thermos! The guy brought his lunch from home and was ashamed to eat it in the office, for fear of being kidded. So he decided a phone booth would do nicely—he just closed the door and nobody ever bothered him. This was my 'prime suspect' for a week!"

The two friends laughed and ordered another cup of coffee.

"How are you doing down at the courts, Dave?" asked Terry. "Meeting any interesting people?"

"Don't think you've cornered the market on screwballs," replied David, "I run into a few beauts of my own. We have a batch of regulars at Criminal Courts."

"Well, well," Mulligan smiled, "welcome to the fraternity!"

"I'm an unwilling member." David laughed. "We've got us the hallway judges. Really, they're harmless—but they drive me nuts. It's a batch of men who have made the courts their hobby. Most of them are middle-aged and some are elderly. I'd guess the majority are retired, probably on small pensions, and the one thing they've got is plenty of time. So they go to court. They've been going for so many years they know the terminology and procedure as well as the lawyers. And they heckle—in a legal way, of course. During a recess, when we're trying to interview somebody in the hall, they're buttonholing anybody who will listen and get going with, 'This case will never stand up on appeal if there's a conviction' or 'The judge should never have allowed that evidence to go into the record.' Sometimes they're right—but I'm not there to make conversation with them—I try to use the short recess time to get hold of people I may not be able to reach later. And with them in full voice there, it's really like trying to break through the sound barrier."

"Ah," Terry chuckled, "let the poor old codgers alone. It's an elevating hobby and it's free."

"I wouldn't care what they did, if they only did it quietly. You should sit in front of them in court when a witness is talking in a low voice and three of them fall asleep and start to snore! Although I will say, in all fairness, that mostly they cork off when the trial gets dull."

"There you are," said Terry, rising, "you've got your own critics' circle and you're complaining!"

David rose also and the two men walked out into the night.

As Mulligan shook hands with David, he said, "Tell you what, Dave. Why don't we make a night of it soon—you and your girl, and my wife and I?"

"Sounds O.K. to me." David smiled. "Let me know when you can make it. Alice would love to meet you—she's heard a lot about you."

Terry grinned. "Nice name, Alice. O.K., boy—fine. I'll call you as soon as I have some time off."

✰✰✰ 33

THE THINGS THEY LEAVE IN TAXIS

FRED CARSTAIRS, the city's best-known racketeer, got careless one afternoon. As a result of his momentary lapse, he sued the city, got a mess of bad publicity, and wound up losing about thirty thousand dollars. A less flamboyant result was a feature piece by David, the idea for which stemmed from the Carstairs story.

The gambler, who was addicted to taxis, left a brown Manila envelope in one. When he discovered his loss, he went down to the Police Property Clerk's office and put in a claim for it. Had it been any one but Carstairs, the matter would have been routine. But the unpretentious brown envelope contained $30,250 in cash, and its claimant and owner was well known as a gambler. The police refused to give it back unless he could prove that he came by it honestly.

The gambler was outraged and sued the city. Eventually, he won his suit, but it was a hollow victory: he had presented the honest cab driver with $3,000; the federal government came around with liens for back income taxes, plus interest, to the tune of $26,000; there were court costs and legal fees. There were even those who contended that Carstairs would have been ahead of the game had he simply let the whole thing ride, but Mr. Carstairs averred piously that there was a principal involved.

It was while the story was on the front pages that David decided to take a closer look at the Property Clerk's office—and wound up spending the better part of the day there.

"I couldn't tear myself away," he told Alice at dinner that night. "That place is absolutely incredible—I could write a book about it!"

"A book's too long," Alice laughed, "try a feature."

"It's been done before," replied David, "but maybe I could find a new angle. The Carstairs story ought to give it a peg."

"What do they have there?" asked Alice curiously.

"Practically everything listed in a mail order catalog—in addition to a few custom-made items. There are over fifty sets of false teeth, plus a half-dozen head rugs."

"Head rugs?" Alice was puzzled.

"Toupees," explained David patiently. "Men are entitled to their vanities, too, although few are reclaimed. I'd guess most of them belong to men in the public eye and they're afraid of ridicule in the press if they went to reclaim them. They're awfully good jobs, though. I'd guess each cost about $300 apiece to make. . . ."

"Why are you so interested in toupees?" queried Alice. She cocked a speculative eye at his thick crop of brown hair. "Are you worried about losing yours?"

He laughed. "You never know!"

"What have they got there besides teeth and hair? Anything I'd be interested in?"

"Are you interested in diamond clips, sables, jewelry, money?"

"Oh, my—yes!" Alice brightened. "Do you mean to tell me people lose things like that and don't call for them?"

"Sometimes. Supposing a man goes to a hockey game with the boys and loses his wallet. In order to reclaim it, he must give full information to the Police Property Clerk—including where and when it was lost. And supposing this gentleman told his wife he was sitting up with a sick friend—because she wanted him to spend the evening playing bridge with some particularly dull neighbors. Then he had to decide—what's more important, his money back or peace in his home? So now you know how money goes unclaimed."

Alice wrinkled her nose distastefully. "Sometimes I have a low opinion of people," she sniffed.

"Don't!" David laughed. "Maybe the guy who found it needs it a lot more. And if it's not claimed for ninety days— finders keepers."

"Does that go for everything?"

"For everything that isn't found by a policeman or a fireman. Anything they find that isn't claimed is sold at public auction, the proceeds going to the Police Department's Benevolent Society."

"Were there really fur coats there, or are you pulling my leg?" demanded Alice.

"I'm not kidding," replied David earnestly. "They have a huge, moth-proof closet—almost a room—and there was about $150,000 worth of fur coats there, still unclaimed. Many looked new to me. They were left in taxicabs, railroad stations, and cocktail lounges and tea shoppes."

Alice was lost in reverie. "Imagine having so much money, you could forget a mink coat somewhere and not even miss it!" she mused.

"You should see the rest of the stuff waiting there—thousands of lost umbrellas, portfolios, suitcases, crutches, braces, books, handbags, canned goods, shirts, violins—oh boy, what a mess!"

"I can understand the umbrellas and books—I've lost my share of those" commented Alice. "But braces? And crutches? How do you forget those?"

"That's not unusual. You know what else they have there? A tremendous stuffed alligator, two bass fiddles, urns with human ashes, a couple of tombstones and a skeleton, like the

ones used in medical schools!" He took his notebook out of
his pocket. "Let's see, did I forget anything."

"Oh, no!" protested Alice hastily. "That's enough. The
place sounds like a madhouse."

"They keep order, all right. You know, just because there's
no claimant for some of the publicized things—like jewelry
or expensive furs—doesn't mean that people don't try. Every
time an item appears in the papers about some fabulous knick-
knack found by a bus boy, about twenty people show up to
say, 'it's mine!' Of course they must offer proof—a bill of sale,
an accurate description. And all they know is what they've
read in the papers, although some of them try to bull their way
through. They don't get far, though—the Property Clerk has
been in the job for twenty-five years and he can smell a
phoney."

"Good for him!" declared Alice spiritedly. "If these people
put forth half as much energy toward acquiring something
honestly—! Really, sometimes I almost hate people!"

David tweaked her hair. "No, you don't," he said gently.
"The trouble with you is that you love them—and it bothers
you when they act beastly. You want them to be perfect."

"It's all right with me if you want to attribute to me virtues
I do not have," scoffed Alice. "But I know what I mean," she
added sternly. But she was pleased with what David had said
about her, nevertheless. It showed in her shining eyes.

"You know what bothers me?" asked David. "That darned
stuffed alligator! How could anyone forget a stuffed alligator?
Big, ugly beast, too."

Alice giggled. "I'm developing a theory about that, which
I'll tell you, if you're interested. As a matter of fact, I'll tell
you anyway. There's this man, see, who's an explorer-type and
a big bore about it. The kind who shoots once and talks about
it endlessly. Anyhow, once in his youth he made a lucky shot
and netted this alligator and brought the skin home to show to

his wife. Then he had it stuffed and put it over the fireplace in the den. And as the years went by, his wife detested more and more the sight of that ugly thing up there, gathering dust and looking dreadful among all her nice chintz covers. So one day she got her courage up, then she climbed up there and took that darn thing down. She wrapped it up and took a taxi and deliberately left it there. And good for her!"

David laughed. "You're not so original, you know. Believe it or not, the Property Clerk advanced almost the exact theory!"

Back in his apartment that night, David wrote a short, amusing piece on the things people leave behind in taxis. Holloway ran it later in the week and it made an amusing side story to the Carstairs trial.

☆☆☆ *34*

DAVID MAKES HIS TELEVISION DEBUT

ONE AFTERNOON David returned to the *Ledger* office to find a notice in his mailbox. "Call Miss Schaeffer of WAJC-TV" and a phone number. Puzzled, he dialed the number and asked for the lady in question.

It developed that Miss Schaeffer was secretary to Art Cranston, who produced the "Answer the Press" television program. Mr. Cranston would like David to be a member of the panel of newspaper men who would interview Chester Marsh, the city's Commissioner of Trade, on next Sunday's program. Would David be interested?

David managed to keep the excitement out of his voice as he allowed yes, he would. Before he could ask any further questions, Miss Schaeffer thanked him and said a letter would go out in the mail that very afternoon, giving him full details as to time and studio. Then she rang off.

David had bought a small television set shortly after he acquired his apartment. He watched it infrequently, but one program he tried to catch regularly was "Answer the Press" a program which was broadcast locally every Sunday afternoon, in which people currently in the public eye were questioned by a varying panel of newspapermen. Sometimes, when extremely sharp questions were put to the guest, the program was very exciting. But frequently David watched it wth a good deal of frustration when the newspapermen, for reasons of their own, did not pursue a line of questioning which promised to be quite revealing.

David, fearing that perhaps Miss Schaeffer might change her mind, decided to say nothing about the telephone call until the formal invitation to appear on the program arrived in the mail. It came promptly the next day, however, giving the address of the studio, mentioning that the program went on the air at 3:30 p.m., and requesting David's arrival at three. There was also a casual mention that there would be an "honorarium" of twenty-five dollars.

Alice laughed when she read the letter. "If they paid a decent sum, they'd use the word 'fee.' It's a good, honest, unequivocating word. With only a twenty-five dollar payment, they have to hide behind 'honorarium'!"

"You're much too mercenary," David scolded her. "Anyhow, I don't care about the money—I only hope I don't make an ass of myself. I've never made a public appearance. Supposing I open my mouth and words won't come out? Or through sheer nervousness, I mispronounce some simple word?"

"You won't," Alice reassured him, "because you'll research this just as you would if you were going to interview him alone and without cameras. You'll have a list of questions, and you can put it on the table in front of you. And one more thing!" her voice rose ominously. "If you try to be a 'gentleman' with our Commissioner of Trade and not ask him anything embarrassing, I'll never forgive you. I think the man is a crook and I'd like him to answer some pointed questions!"

"Don't worry," replied David evenly. "I don't know about the other reporters, but he'll get some interesting questions from me. It's just too bad that this one rotten apple has to give all the city's honest commissioners a bad name. I looked through his clips last night, and I found a few which are very old. . . ." He smiled enigmatically.

Alice looked at him searchingly and then returned his smile. "Go to it, boy—and good luck!"

Marsh, the Commissioner of Trade, had been in the news the previous two weeks on charges that he had played favorites in awarding city contracts. He, of course, denied this vehemently, pointing to his twenty years in public office—"public service," as he put it. The record showed that, while he had not done anything to disgrace himself in those years, neither had he accomplished anything of outstanding merit. He was another hack in office, well-connected politically, with a garrulous tongue and the slick politician's ability to squeeze out of tight situations.

In addition to reading all the data available in the *Ledger's* morgue, David also checked with the paper's City Hall man. Since the Marsh business was really a City Hall scandal, David was somewhat embarrassed about calling a fellow reporter who had all the facts at his finger tips. They should have invited him on the program, not me, thought David. He's familiar with it. His colleague sensed David's feeling and put him at his ease. "I guess they wanted a new face on that show and, besides, I've been on it plenty of times. So relax—you're not cutting me out."

David sighed with relief, and the City Hall man filled him in. "Marsh is no fool. Lots of people think he's long-winded and obtuse and all he's doing is being sharp. You'll notice he's not a bit windy when there's a point he wants to make. Incidentally," his mentor warned David, "you may find the other reporters will take it very easy with him—it's something which exasperates me here, too."

"Why?" asked David, mystified.

"I don't know—he has probably done them some favors, maybe gotten a job for a relative. Or else they just don't want trouble. In any case, don't let them throw you."

"Don't worry," replied David, "I won't!"

David got to the studio, which was located in midtown, about an hour ahead of time. He was so early that nobody connected with the show was there yet. They started traipsing in shortly after three o'clock.

On the panel with David were reporters from two other newspapers. One of them David had met briefly a few months before; he was introduced to the other. They acknowledged him coolly. Both had made frequent prior appearances on the program and conducted themselves with the ease of TV veterans. With the arrival of Marsh, all four of them, including Art Cranston, the program's moderator, were ushered in turn toward a modified barber's chair, where pancake make-up was applied by a pretty young woman. Cranston introduced David to the Commissioner of Trade, who acknowledged him warily. Marsh then turned effusively toward the other two reporters, who were obviously well known to him. They greeted him warmly and the three of them chatted familiarly.

As David stood there, uncomfortably alone in the midst of a loquacious group, he watched the make-up being applied by the nimble fingers of the young make-up artist. He noted with amusement how she used a much darker shade to cover the receding hairline of one of the reporters and felt a vain satisfaction when she looked speculatively toward him, the last one, then sealed off the dark-hued tin and put it away.

In a minute she beckoned to him. David eased himself into the chair, his collar open and his tie loosened, and gave himself up to the embarrassing ministrations of the young lady. Regardless of the savoir-faire of his colleagues, he felt plain foolish. He looked at her sheepishly. She smiled broadly and winked. "Just forget you've got it on," she advised. "You won't look made-up on camera, but without it you'd look washed out."

Three minutes before air time the five men took their assigned seats at a longish table. Chester Marsh sat at one end and the three reporters and Art Cranston a short distance away. On the desk, facing toward the camera, there was a name plate for each person, indicating the affiliation. Opposite David's chair, the plate read: DAVID WHITE, *New York Ledger*.

Art Cranston explained that he would like to give all the reporters a chance to ask their questions and he requested them, in turn, to please wait until they were recognized before speaking.

Then there was a rapid blinking red signal light, and they were on the air.

Cranston introduced Chester Marsh, briefly mentioned the charges made against him and asked for questions.

David shot his hand up, but the first series of questions went to one of the other reporters. "Mr. Commissioner," he asked, "isn't it a common hazard of public office to answer charges that are made from time to time?"

This was the kind of loaded question David detested. In the first place, it was more a statement than it was a question. Second, the facetious quality of the "question" implied that all such charges—and these in particular—were baseless.

The commissioner took his cue quickly. He laughed jovially and launched into a three-minute exposition on the difficulties of public office. When he finished, David put his hand up again. This time the floor was given to his other colleague, who pursued the original line of questioning.

"Mr. Commissioner, would you say these charges are politically inspired?"

Of course, once again the commissioner was launched. This time he sniped at some political opponents who had triggered the charges, and continued, "This is nothing but politics—gutter politics. In my four years as Commissioner of Trade, I have never favored anybody. I have always awarded contracts to the lowest bidder!"

Almost a third of the program was over before David was finally recognized.

"Mr. Commissioner, er . . ." David began haltingly, then quickly recovered. "How many contracts have you awarded to the Gray-Green Trucking Company since you've been in office?"

The commissioner looked at him haughtily. "I haven't the vaguest idea," he replied coolly. "I will say this—every contract they got they were entitled to. There was no funny business. There was no payment under the table or anything like that."

"You mean there were no kickbacks, Mr. Commissioner?"

"That's exactly what I mean!"

"Well, sir, would I be fairly accurate if I said the records in the *Ledger* library show that the Gray-Green Trucking Company has received more than eighty contracts from you?"

"I haven't counted them. I don't know. That may be right. What difference does it make anyway, young man?"

"I'll get to that a little later, sir. But in the meantime—was there closed bidding on these jobs?"

"Of course!"

"How many firms entered bids?"

"I don't know—maybe half a dozen or so." The commissioner was irritated and impatient at this line of questioning and looked toward Cranston, the moderator, to stop it. But David was entitled to finish his series of questions and Cranston blandly ignored Marsh.

David's polite voice continued, "And the Gray-Green Company was always the lowest bidder?"

"That's right." The commissioner was exasperated. "Wait a minute—now and then another company came in with a lower bid, but they were unable to convince me that they were able to do the job properly. I felt, and this was in my discretion as commissioner, that they would cost the city more money in the long run."

"Mr. Commissioner, are you familiar with the city's conflict of interest law?"

"Of course, I am. Why?"

And then David uncapped the fuse on his stored dynamite. In an ingenuous voice he asked, "Is your wife's maiden name Kenmore?"

"Er, yes, that's right." The commissioner's eyes narrowed and his mouth became a thin, angry line. "What about it?"

"Is she an officer of the Gray-Green Trucking Company, Mr. Commissioner?"

"Just a minute!" The commissioner was controlling himself —but just barely. "Sure my wife is an officer of that company —she was with that company even before we were married, twenty-four years ago! What's that got to do with me? I don't work for the company—my wife does. That's no violation of the conflict of interest law! Gray-Green got those contracts on merit, and on nothing else!"

The commissioner went on that way for fully three minutes —and the more he expostulated, the more ridiculous his argument looked. David had no further questions. His two colleagues attempted lamely to save the situation by reverting once again to "political enemies" but the die was cast.

When the show finally ended, David walked up to the commissioner to say good-bye, but Marsh glared venomously at
him and turned his back, pretending not to see the young
reporter's proffered hand. David shrugged and went to wash
off his make-up. Then he headed for a phone.

"How was it, Alice?" he asked.

She chortled with glee. "You were sensational, Davey!"
He could hear her parents in the background. "Tell him he was
the best thing on in weeks," her father was saying. "Dave?"
Alice laughed, "when you got that last question in, you looked
just exactly like the cat that ate the canary! And so handsome!"

The TV station which had recorded the show sent out a full
text of the interview over its own wires, which went into the
office of every newspaper in town. It was a tremendous thrill
for David to read in Monday morning's papers the questions
he had put to the commissioner and the replies which had been
given. The *Ledger* story even pointed out that the salient questions were put by their own reporter, David White.

☆☆☆ *35*

NO BYLINE, PLEASE

WHILE EVERYBODY LIKES to see his name in print, with
lawyers, David found, the desire came close to a passion. They
couldn't really be blamed. Lawyers, like doctors, are not supposed to advertise. Therefore, when their names appeared in
print it was, in effect, money in the bank.

In Manhattan, the district attorney had eighty-five assistants, and the more prominent or notorious cases were invariably handled by the department heads themselves, such as the Chief of Rackets, Indictment, Fraud, Homicide Bureaus, etc. Since the salary was very modest, most of the assistant district attorneys planned to stay in that job for only a few years— until they'd made a "name" for themselves. Consequently, the more publicity they got, the better it would serve them when they went into private practice, the theory being that clients would come a-running.

Similarly, lawyers already in private practice took the view that, as their names became known through frequent appearances in print, potential defendants would recall this and call on them when in need.

This situation, of course, culminated in a mutual-aid society, also known as one-hand-washes-the-other. Assistant d.a.'s cautiously established a rapport with those reporters they could trust not to betray them and, from time to time, passed along a nugget of secret information. It was understood that at some future date the reporter would repay the favor by mentioning the informant's name—in connection with another story, of course. Lawyers in private practice did the same thing.

Since David represented one of the largest and most respected newspapers in the city, he was in an especially good position. He did, however, have to use a lot of judgment and discretion. In these instances, there were frequently times when no honor existed among the thieves. Lawyers had been known to pass along phoney tips; in fact, there were times when they invented them. And so David became a shrewd judge of legal horseflesh. He got so he could almost smell a phoney tip, and his instinct on a man's trustworthiness became keen and sure.

He had established a close rapport with several of the assistant d.a.'s who had handled a few fairly well-publicized trials. They (each unknown to the others, of course) became his contacts. One of these was Sam Wilson, a young assistant in the Rackets Bureau. Sam was a good lawyer; through his ingenuity and clever examination of both prosecution and defense witnesses in a shakedown case, he had been successful in winning a conviction against a notorious waterfront racketeer—to the shocked amazement of defense counsel, a wily veteran of the courts.

David was so impressed with the job Wilson did that, when writing up the story of the conviction, he referred to the youthful assistant prosecutor as "a scourge of racketeers." Pleased as punch, Sam telephoned David the next day to thank him profusely.

Of course, there were cases where defense counsel made prosecution witnesses look silly, and David reported that with equal impartiality.

Either way, the lawyers needed the press. Even those attorneys high up on the rung liked to get their names in print for, as David paraphrased the poem one night to Alice, "Breathes there a lawyer with soul so dead, who never to himself hath said, 'I want to be a judge'?" The answer was "no." And the politicians in power, who name prospective members of the judiciary, like to select some one whose name is known.

When something big was about to break, there was always a restless atmosphere around the courts. The assistant d.a.'s averted their eyes when approached by members of the press, for the district attorney ruled his flock like an autocratic monarch; he made the rules and heaven help any of his subjects who disobeyed them. The Number One rule was—*All information will emanate from the district attorney only!*

A major scandal was due to be exposed; the grand jury had been investigating a top official in the Fire Department on extortion charges. And since the grand jury minutes are secret, that was all David and the other members of the press corps knew, officially. Of course, they suspected a good deal more. On a hunch, David telephoned Sam Wilson.

The assistant d.a. was cagey. "I'm going down for a coffee break in about ten minutes."

David named three places, slowly, "The cafeteria? Pommery's? Marshall's?"

At the last place, Wilson interjected a casual, "Yes."

"Good," replied David. "I'll meet you there."

Fifteen minutes later, the two men were seated at a back table in a small coffee shop. "You should know better than to question me on the telephone!" chided the young lawyer.

It was true, David reflected, he should know better. No lawyer in his right mind would ever discuss anything of a confidential nature over the telephone. They were too afraid of wire taps.

And so began a very edifying and highly private conversation. It ended in promises of mutual confidence, and David didn't bother returning to the pressroom. Instead, he headed right for the *Ledger*.

Holloway listened to him intently. "You sure of this?" he asked.

"Positive," replied David. "But to protect Wilson, perhaps you'd better not put my name on the story. The d.a. knows we're friendly and he'd trace the leak back to him."

"You're right," agreed Holly. "We'll put Guy Waldron's name on this. You'd better break the news to him—it'll be a real surprise. He hasn't been near the courts in fifteen years!"

David went over to his desk and wrote his story. After he had dropped it at the city desk, he walked over to Guy Waldron, who worked on rewrite, and explained the situation. "That's O.K. with me." Waldron laughed. "That's the kind of story I like best—no work and all byline."

At dinner with Alice that night, David explained how it

happened that he had written an exclusive story for Monday's paper in which he had requested anonymity.

"That's a new twist," commented Alice. "You get an exclusive and you don't want the credit?"

"I'm getting the credit where it's important—with Holly," explained David. "As for the rest of the town—it's more important to me to protect Sam Wilson. And if the d.a. knew I wrote the story, he'd go after Sam's head."

"Look, Davey—I lost you ten minutes ago. You'd better start at the beginning."

"O.K. It's no secret that a grand jury has been investigating an official in the Fire Department for some time. There have been several stories on that in recent weeks. He's been suspected of running a $1,000,000 a year racket—forcing installers of oil burners to pay him a fixed sum before his inspectors approved their installations. Well, the grand jury indicted him today, but the story won't be given out by the district attorney until Monday."

"If the grand jury indicted him today, why isn't it being announced today?" Alice asked reasonably.

"Because today is Friday, my naive one, and if he announced it today, it would appear in the late editions of today's afternoon papers and in Saturday's morning papers. The circulation of papers on Saturday is the lowest of the week. Whereas if he announces it on Monday, it will get a big play in the late afternoon papers on that day, as well as the Tuesday morning papers. That's why. Our d.a., when he makes a coup of this size, likes to get the largest possible circulation."

Alice laughed. "Everybody wants to be a judge!"

David smiled in accord. "Really, he's entitled to a big play. An awful lot of hard work went into breaking this case."

"How did you hear about it?" asked Alice.

"Sam Wilson tipped me off this afternoon. Of course, I couldn't use his name in the story—it would be a dead give-away. I'll make it up to him another day." David grinned in anticipation. "Oh, boy—wait till the *Ledger* hits the news-stands on Sunday night with the story. The d.a. has already announced a press conference for 10 a.m. Monday. What's he going to tell the boys in the pressroom?—'read the details in this morning's *Ledger'?*" He chortled with glee.

"Tell me, David," Alice was curious. "Are you interfering with the investigation in any way by printing such a story before it is publicly announced?"

David was indignant. "Of course not. If I thought so, I wouldn't print it. The indictment has been voted, so by my saying so I'm not hindering justice in any way. As a matter of fact, I also know that the Fire Department official has al-ready been told of the indictment through his lawyer, and he has been told to be in court on Monday, to be arraigned on the indictment."

"Then the story was conceivably available through the official's lawyer?" asked Alice.

"Yes. But not very likely," conceded David. "A lawyer will tip you off to good news on his client, but rarely on bad news."

"If the story was available through the lawyer, as well as the d.a.'s office, then why didn't you want a byline?" pursued Alice.

"I told you," explained David patiently, "to protect Sam. If the d.a. sees my name on it, he'll know that one of his as-sistants fed me. He'll suspect me anyway—but with Lou Car-roll's name on the story, he'll be thrown off, maybe."

Promptly at 10 a.m. Monday, David walked in with the other reporters for the district attorney's scheduled press con-ference. Spread out full length on the d.a.'s desk was that morning's *Ledger*. The lead story on page 1 had a three-column headline dealing with the indictment of the Fire Department official.

"Who's been feeding the *Ledger?*" The question was angrily directed to the d.a. by a *Transcript* reporter.

"That's what I'd like to know," snapped the d.a., shooting a searching glance at David. "I have a very good hunch as to who wrote this story!"

"Don't look at me," said David tranquilly. "Lou Carroll's name is on the story, and I've been off all week end. By the way," he querried offhandedly, "is the article accurate?"

"It certainly is," fumed the d.a., "and that's another reason I feel you wrote it—and I don't care whose name is on it! It showed knowledge which did not come out of any files, and information which came from somebody who had been following this case closely from its inception." His sharp blue eyes held David like a trap.

David met the onslaught unwaveringly. "Did the article hurt your case in any way?" he asked quietly.

"No," admitted the d.a. grudgingly. Then he looked around the room menacingly, "but I'm supposed to be the one who gives out the news around here—nobody else! It's going to be just too bad if it develops that one of my assistants is the source of the leak. I know I can't do anything to a reporter for printing a story ahead of time—but I can straighten out anybody in this office who doesn't live by my rules!"

The district attorney then proceeded to give the details of the indictment to all the reporters at the press conference—details which had appeared that morning in the *Ledger*—and which the American Press had picked up from the paper's first edition and had put on its wires, with credit to the *Ledger*.

"How did it go?" Alice asked David when he returned to the office that evening. "Is the d.a. going to hold you in contempt or something?"

"He'll get over it," said David, smiling broadly. "I could make him even madder by writing now that he confirmed a story which had already appeared in the *Ledger!*"

GYP STORES

DAVID'S WRISTWATCH HAD BEEN acting up of recent weeks, and one morning it stopped altogether. He kept forgetting to bring it in for repairs and then one day, while walking down Broadway toward the *Ledger* office, on his way from Criminal Courts in the late afternoon, he passed a small shop with hundreds of watches in the window. These were all but obliterated by monstrous signs—SELLING OUT, PRACTICALLY GIVING THEM AWAY, etc. David was not ordinarily a bargain hunter, but the price, $3.71 caught his eye. This was less than the repair of his old watch would be. Almost before he knew it, he went in and made the purchase.

After he had written his story, he walked over to Alice's desk and showed his new watch to her. "Oh, David—that was a silly thing to do!" she reproved him.

"Why?" he asked defensively. "It was only $3.71—or rather $4.64, with taxes! It's assembly-line stuff but I don't care. It works!"

"If it runs for a week, I'll eat your hat! You ought to know better than to go into those gyp stores!"

David's enthusiasm for his purchase waned rapidly. He laughed sheepishly. "Oh, well, I didn't get stuck for so very much!"

Alice's prediction proved right as rain. By noon the next day, David's watch showed 10:10, and by four p.m. it had simply expired. David fished out the receipt from his jacket pocket and stalked into the store.

"I only bought this watch yesterday," he explained, "and it's stopped dead!"

The clerk was indifferent. "Did you read your guarantee?"

David unfolded the small square of print and read:

Mail the watch to us for adjustment with $1.00 to cover the cost of repair and twenty-five cents for handling, packing and return postage. This guarantee is void if watch has been tampered with, taken apart, wet, repaired by anyone but ourselves or mistreated in any form. If this watch is beyond repair, it will be returned to you in the same condition as received. All repairs must be shipped parcel post, prepaid insured. Your guarantee must accompany this watch. Do not return it to store where purchased, but direct to Authorized Repair Service.

David reddened with anger. "Why, this is nothing but a big gyp," he told the clerk. "I'm to pay half the price of the watch, just to mail it to this place, and the chances are it may be returned to me in the same condition as it is now. And it's not even twenty-four hours old!"

The clerk shrugged and walked off to attend to some customers who had just entered the store. David stood there fuming for a while and then stormed out.

Back at the *Ledger,* he strode over to Alice's desk. She was in conversation with her boss, Mark Cornish, the Sunday editor.

"Meet the country yokel who got taken by the city slicker," he greeted them ironically and flipped the watch and the "guarantee" on Alice's desk. The hands of the watch were immobilized for all time at four o'clock. Alice shook her head slowly from side to side, and Cornish picked up the two items and examined them. "I bought it yesterday," explained David.

"These stores are a disgrace to the city," snapped Mr. Cornish, angrily. "The legitimate stores suffer because of them.

A number of them are even mushrooming up on Fifth Avenue!" He stood in silent thought for a while and then came to a decision.

"David," he said, "I'd like you to do a piece for the Sunday paper on the gyp stores. Find out what the city is doing about them, and what measures the legitimate businessmen are taking. Check with the Better Business Bureau, the Fifth Avenue Association and the Broadway Association. If these clip joints can't be put out of business, at least we can warn our readers about them."

He turned to Alice. "Call Teddy Gleason and tell him to get a couple of good pictures for me. Tell him to check with David. Incidentally," he added, a twinkle in his eye, "you could probably help your boy friend here a good deal by going around with him. They might be suspicious of a good-looking young guy marching around by himself, but when a couple comes in arm-in-arm, everybody assumes they parked their wits at home."

Alice brightened. "It sounds like fun," she said. "And besides, I've always wanted to be a leg man."

Mr. Cornish lowered his gaze. "Well, you've certainly got the equipment," he said appreciatively and headed back into his own office.

"He's a dear." Alice laughed fondly. "Every now and then he says something personal and then runs for his life!" She turned to David with enthusiasm. "When do we start?"

"Saturday is probably the best time," he replied. "I want to make a few calls and get a line on some stores which are frequent offenders, and we'll hit those first. Boy," he added with feeling, "this is one story I'm really going to enjoy writing!"

On the phone and through personal interview, David dealt with officialdom and discovered the usual amount of buckpassing. The stores operate just this side of the law, so the law-

makers contended they were helpless—or almost so. The land-
lords could put a stop to the racket by refusing to rent to shady
enterprises; but a landlord who is receiving a fantastic rent
for his premises is not too fussy about his tenant's ethics. One
inspector in charge of the bureau whose function it was to
police these stores put the blame squarely on the customer.

"Everybody wants something for nothing," he said cynically.
"There are people who would pay two dollars for a ten-cent
tea strainer provided there was a tag on it saying 'Reduced
from $20'!"

When he met Alice on Saturday, David produced a list of
store names and addresses. "Every one of these has a complaint
lodged against it, but this one" he pointed to one which was
underlined, "has a dossier as long as your arm. Two weeks
ago," he explained, "the daughter of a prominent New Jersey
attorney bought a large tablecloth and six napkins here. At
least, she thought she had. When she got home, she realized
she had been a 'switch victim'—the tablecloth was half the
size she had stipulated, and so were the napkins. She had a
sales receipt, but all it said was, 'tablecloth and six napkins.'
Her father brought the receipt and items to every civic organization in the city. Eventually, the store gave her what she'd
paid for. Then she had it appraised and found it was worth
a little more than half of what she'd paid for it!"

Alice was exasperated. "I don't know why anybody in his
right mind would walk into a store like this. Look at it!" They
had now arrived at their destination. The store front was emblazoned with huge signs, similar to the gift shop where David
had bought his bargain watch. Only this was a linen shop.
One legend read: PURE BELGIAN LINEN. Then there was
a large $83 with a thin line running through it and underneath,
$37.

"It's probably worth all of eight dollars," muttered Alice.

"Come now," caroled David. "Wipe that intelligent look off your face and let's see the simpering fiancée emerge!"

Alice obediently crossed her eyes and let her lower jaw slacken.

David laughed. "Not so much—let's not frighten the men, dear," he admonished, and the young couple sauntered slowly into the store, arm-in-arm.

Inside, the floor was littered with torn paper. The salesman, with a harassed manner, apologized for the store's untidy appearance, explaining that they had been so busy, there'd been no time to clean it up. Then he smiled cheerfully at the pair.

Alice diffidently asked to see a linen tablecloth.

Before they knew it, the salesman had pulled several telegrams from his pocket, ostensibly from creditors and the landlord, dunning the tenant for overdue moneys. As he talked, he opened a large green tablecloth—pure linen, he said. The tag read $53. As a special offer, and because of the dire need for cash, they could have it for $19. He mentioned this figure loudly enough to be heard by a colleague.

Promptly, and on cue, the other salesman stormed over.

"Are you offering this for nineteen?" the second salesman asked, with an air of incredulity. "Are you crazy? Go ahead—give the whole darn store away. But I'm warning you—we'll both be fired. That's half what the cloth cost wholesale!"

Alice and David were as fascinated at this byplay as theatergoers at a good drama.

Alice examined the cloth carefully, then murmured something about the color. She turned her blue eyes, innocent of any expression, on the salesman. "Would you have a softer green? Perhaps something more on the aqua side?" As he turned to bring out additional wares, Alice nudged David sharply and the two beat a hasty retreat out into the Fifth Avenue sunshine.

Outside, Alice exploded with anger. "How stupid did he

think we were?" she demanded.

"You looked real stupid," David told her admiringly.

"Thanks!" she snapped. Then both of them burst into laughter.

"Come on," said Alice. "I want to show you something."

They walked a few blocks north on Fifth Avenue and then Alice led David into one of the fine department stores of the city. They pushed their way through the Saturday throng of shoppers, crowded into an elevator and emerged on the fifth floor, where the store had its linen department. They strolled down the aisle while Alice's expert eye traveled along the shelves until she found what she had been looking for.

"May we see that cloth, please?" She pointed it out to the salesgirl, who took it down. It was an exact duplicate of the one the gyp store salesman had shown them. It was cotton, not linen, and the price was plainly printed on a small square of paper stapled in the corner: $6.95.

"Is this the same thing?" asked David.

"Identical," replied Alice. "There's a tremendous difference between linen and cotton. The nerve of him, thinking I couldn't tell them apart!"

David made a few penciled notes in his book, then tucked it back in his pocket. "It's your own fault," he told her as they walked toward the elevator. "Who would think that a girl as pretty as you would also be bright?"

Outside, they resumed their quest, with time out for lunch.

On the other side of the street, they passed another "bargain" linen store. "Look at that!" Alice exclaimed.

There were towels displayed in the window, of an unknown brand with the sign SPECIAL SALE—THICK OVERSIZE BATH TOWELS 59 cents. From the way they were stacked, each towel appeared to be at least four inches thick. Then Alice led David around to the side, to view the towel pyramid at an angle. On close scrutiny, it became evident that each folded towel contained at least six other "thick oversize bath towels" to pad it out!

The pair strolled over to Broadway, where the phoney "gift shops" were doing a rushing business. They walked into a few, inspected some of the items, made a number of inquiries and walked out.

"Now I know what happened to the stuff they used to give away at carnivals," said Alice dryly.

"I've got more than enough material now—I'll write the article tomorrow and give it to Cornish on Monday. I'm yours for the rest of the evening." He turned to Alice. "What would you like to do?"

"Sit down," she replied promptly. "My feet hurt."

It was shortly after five, and the matinee crowds were pouring out of the theaters. As they turned into a side street to avoid the stampede, David spotted a familiar figure standing at the curb, attempting to hail a taxi.

"Gee, he looks familiar," he told Alice as they approached the man. "I can't place him!"

"That's Scott Avery." Alice laughed. "Just ask any woman in the city."

"Of course!" said David. "Mr. Avery! Hi!"

The actor turned around, puzzled, and then recognition came. "Hello, there!" He extended his hand warmly. "You're White—the reporter from the *Ledger*. Good to see you!"

David introduced Scott Avery to Alice and he shook hands with her. "Your pal here," he told her, "picked me up out of the mud at Jackson Airport and now, every time I pick up the *Transcript,* I feel guilty!"

They all laughed.

"You look a lot better now than you did then," said David.

"I'll bet," agreed the actor. "Look—would you like to see the show tonight?"

David looked at Alice. Would they! The actor was making

his debut in a musical role, for a change, and the show, which had only opened a month ago, was a sell-out. In addition to Avery, an outstanding comedienne and other top-flight performers were in the cast.

"Why, we'd love to," replied David.

"Fine—I'll tell you what—I'll leave four tickets in your name at the box office. Now, please excuse me," the actor was apologetic, "but my wife will have hysterics if I don't get home fast. I've had a number of TV shows and rehearsals during the past two weeks and I've hardly been home at all." A cab pulled up. Avery extended his hand once more, "I'm awfully glad I ran into you again." He smiled warmly. "I hope you'll enjoy the show."

"I'm sure we will," replied David. "And thanks!"

The taxi pulled away and Alice, her eyes shining, watched it turn the corner.

"What a charming man!" she exclaimed. "I'm drooling!"

"Your feet still hurt?" asked David, amused.

"No, no! They've acquired wings! Who's coming to the show with us?"

David thought a while. "You know? I think I'll try Terry Mulligan. You remember—that detective I told you about? We've been meaning to get together as a foursome. Gosh, I hope he isn't tied up!"

They walked toward a drugstore on the corner of Eighth Avenue and Alice waited while David headed for the phone booth. In a few minutes he emerged, smiling. "We'll meet them in front of the theater at 8:15! And now, my tired little assistant—let us go and have a leisurely dinner." He offered his arm with a stiff and courtly gesture.

"Who's tired?" hooted Alice. "It's the shank of the evening!"

Their seats were excellent and the show was a riot of laughter and music. All four were sorry to have it end.

Afterwards, they went into a little coffee house in the west fifties. Terry's wife, Kathleen, and Alice hit it off well. Both of them were the no-nonsense type, with a dry and keen humor. David told the Mulligans of their afternoon excursion into the gyp stores, and Alice added a number of feminine observations. Before the four parted, they were interruping each other with the practiced ease of long-standing friends.

David wrote the gyp store piece the next day, and Cornish ran it the following Sunday.

☆☆☆ *37*

DAVID WRITES A NARCOTIC SERIES

ONE AFTERNOON, while David was sitting around the pressroom in Criminal Courts, the office called. "Davey?" It was Suzy, the *Ledger* telephone operator. "Mr Holloway says, if you're not doing much, come on up to the office. He wants to talk with you."

"Oh?" asked David. "What about?"

"Search me," replied Suzy airily. "He's probably got a brainstorm."

"Well, there's not a darn thing doing here. Tell him I'll be there in half an hour." Somewhat mystified, David reached for his hat and coat and walked out into the late afternoon haze. He searched his mind for recent stories in which he might have had errors, but dismissed that line of reasoning. Holly was not a petty man—he wouldn't call you into the office to bawl you out. I wonder what's up, he thought.

He found out soon enough.

Holly was on a phone when David entered the city room, but he spotted the young reporter immediately and beckoned him over with his free hand. He grunted monosyllabically into the phone, indicating a desire to terminate the conversation. This was soon done and he turned to David.

"What do you know about dope?" he opened abruptly.

"Dope?" David repeated. "You mean heroin, morphine and all that?"

"That's exactly what I mean."

"Very little," replied David honestly. "Why?"

"You're going to do a series on it for the *Ledger*."

"Me?" David groped frantically for words. "But I know practically nothing on the subject. Wouldn't Dick Ewell be the man for that?" Dick was the *Ledger's* medical reporter.

"No—and for the very reason you think he would. He's too close to the subject. I'd wind up with a medical report." Holly inclined his shaggy head toward David. "I'm taking you off the courts for the next couple of weeks. There's nothing much on the calendar anyway. You go hustle yourself around the city and wherever else you have to and find out what's doing with drug addiction—the teen-age angle, what's doing, if anything, in the high schools, the amount of drugs around and so forth."

David gulped. "How much would you want?" he asked.

"How do I know?" roared Holloway. "Depends on what you dig up!" He picked up some copy laying on his desk, indicating the interview was over.

David got weakly to his feet. First stop was obviously the library, to check the clips. He made an initial stop at the water cooler, however, to wet his suddenly parched throat. Rewrite man Roger Mulvaney was already there. His sharp eyes took David in at a glance.

"What's up, Dave? You look like a lamb being led to the slaughter."

"Truer words were never spoken," replied David, and told Mulvaney of his conversation with Holloway. Mulvaney's shoulders rose to the level of his ears, and he winced in mock pain. "Boy, that's a backbreaker," he said sympathetically.

David spent the rest of the afternoon poring over the huge amount of clippings on drugs. He kept out a few which offered "leads." He had a dinner date with Alice that night, and he glumly told her of his new assignment.

"Well, why are you so upset?" she demanded.

"What do I know about drugs?" retorted David despairingly.

"So you'll find out!" asserted Alice calmly. "There's no reason to be in such a stew! You're just scared because of the word 'series.' Why not look at the happier side of it?" She smiled warmly. "In the first place, it will most certainly be on page one, and it will be ballyhooed in advance. For another, it will take you out of the rut of crime stories and give you a much greater scope. Don't be afraid of it," she looked at him encouragingly. "Look at it this way: it's just another story, only the locale is different. You'll still be interviewing people, and —now that you have more judgment—you'll know which are the sincere ones and which are the headline hunters. Besides, think of the good your exposure may do for young people. Why, just to save one boy from such a future would be worth all the trouble. Oh," her eyes were shining. "What a golden opportunity!"

David looked at her and began to feel sheepish.

"You know something?" he asked, excitement mounting in his voice. "You're dead right!"

They solemnly shook hands on this, and the rest of the dinner was punctuated with talk of the job on hand. David showed Alice some of the clips that had particularly interested him and, as he talked, he was amazed to find that, instinctively, he had already mapped out a plan of action.

"The police department has a narcotics squad, and I'll see the inspector in charge. I also want to talk with a couple of judges who handle a lot of narcotic cases. I want to go out to the new city institution where addicts under twenty-one are being treated. I'll have to talk to a couple of the head-shrinkers to get their views on the 'why' of addiction. And some time during the next two weeks I'll go down to Washington to get some national statistics."

Alice looked at him in amazement. "I thought you said you didn't know how to handle this?"

David looked abashed. "I didn't think I did," he admitted.

In the next few weeks, David lived with the subject of narcotics. And as he came to a deeper understanding of this dreadful scourge, a lot of his previous conceptions on dope went out the window.

He chanced to be at a hospital one night where a long-time addict was being given the "cold turkey" treatment—a complete and abrupt withdrawal from drugs—and the physical torment and anguish of the man seemed too much for any human being to bear. . . . And added to these almost insupportable agonies was—sleeplessness.

No wonder addicts would do almost anything to obtain money for drugs—it was to avoid this!

Reading back through the history of drug addiction, David was amazed to discover that, immediately following the War between the States, addiction was known through the land as the "army disease." Thousands of soldiers were conditioned to morphine by army surgeons and they brought their addiction home. Their kinfolk were quite familiar with it, since morphine was the number one drug of the 1800s. It was reported to cure many ills, such as cancer, asthma, tuberculosis and heart disease, and doctors gave syringes to their patients indiscriminately. Too late they discovered they'd given their patients not a soothing poultice—but a scourge. In the '80s, from the royal courts of Europe to New York's Fifth Avenue, solid gold and silver hypodermic syringes set with jewels and diamonds were flashed. Morphine was fashionable. Thousands of drug users bought their supply openly at the corner pharmacy for a few pennies, and there was no social stigma attached to addiction.

Drugs were indeed a very old story. Before morphine, it was opium itself, from which morphine is derived. The poppy blossom was known to be cultivated for opium seven centuries before the birth of Christ. Today, the traffic was in heroin, the arch-criminal of the narcotics world. An outlaw drug, heroin is far too powerful and dangerous for medical use. And yet it was so easily available that one young addict told David, "You just give me the money and I'll get you as much as you want—within an hour."

One of the things that drove David to near distraction was the conflict of opinions. On the "why" of an addict, one psychiatrist said, "Addiction is a primary manifestation of a character disorder . . . one element in a neurosis or psychosis. Emotionally normal individuals seldom become addicted."

But another, equally prominent psychiatrist said, "A majority of narcotics addicts are average individuals in their mental and moral fundamentals. Among them are many men and women of high ideals and worthy accomplishments. They are normal mentally and morally."

"Where," thought David, "does that leave me?"

The conflict of ideas persisted everywhere. A high official in the school system stated there were no more than twenty-seven users in all the high schools combined. An official in the state government countered that there were twenty-seven in each school!

Again David puzzled—these are two reputable public figures. Which one is right?

Authorities even differed widely on the value of a drug-education program in the schools. This had been instituted comparatively recently, for use in grades seven to twelve, in those localities in the city where it seemed advisable.

Two outstanding federal exports on drugs, backed by powerful women's groups, expressed grave objections to narcotic education in schools. Their well-publicized attitude was, "Many young persons, once their curiosity is aroused, will ignore the warning and will experiment upon themselves, with disastrous results."

To which an outstanding medical education man countered: "There is no indication that one single youngster has become addicted just because of the educational processes. We should look upon this in the same way we look upon biological education. The same hullabaloo was raised twenty-five years ago. . . . It is not what is taught, but how."

Wherever David turned, the contradictions were the same. For every facet of the situation, there were at least two diametrically opposite opinions.

A thoughtful doctor at the city's institution for youthful drug addicts said, "Not one of these boys has a normal emotional background. They are severely disturbed. They have family problems, work problems. For them, drug addiction is a chemical retreat from a repugnant reality. Born and reared in the slums, with no mature goal in keeping with their training, they can, under the influence of drugs, become lawyers, doctors, baseball stars in their opiate dreams. Returning a 'cured' patient to the same environment is like embarking on a long journey via a merry-go-round."

David spent a day at the city institution at which youthful addicts attempted to be cured. "It is an open facility," explained the doctor in charge. "There is nothing compulsory about their staying. About half the patients are self-committed —that is, by the courts, through their parents, and half are sent there directly by the courts after they get into trouble with the law."

The young reporter came away depressed and heartened, in about equal measure. Depressed at the amount of misery which existed, and heartened by the attempts of the farseeing men in charge to inject some hope and happiness into the dreary and tormented lives of the youthful inmates. His notebook was filled with facts: on the public school which was in session just for the inmates, about the physical and mental therapy in use, the excellence of the arts and crafts, and the after-care clinic available for discharged patients. His notebook also held case histories—arrestingly dramatic stories, dispassionately related by the inmates themselves. They talked with David freely and unself-consciously.

About the only phase of his investigation into drugs still remaining was the national and international problem, so David flew to the nation's capitol to interview federal officials.

He established that the medical and scientific needs of the world would be adequately filled with an annual production of 500 tons of opium. Yet 2,000 tons were being produced annually. The excess of 1,500 tons had been going to illegal channels and toward the enslavement of millions throughout the world.

A well-known story in international drug control circles concerned the representative of one of the big opium-producing countries who was asked, "Why doesn't your country stop the traffic in drugs by controlling the growth of the poppy?"

The diplomat eyed his questioner blandly. "If you can suggest another commodity which would bring in a comparable revenue, we would gladly do it."

His statement was more forcefully brought home when David did some figuring and realized that one kilo (thirty-five ounces) of heroin costing about $3,000 in Europe could eventually bring $3,000,000 in this country!

When David attempted to get an estimate from a top federal official on the amount of heroin currently in the country, he once again came up against the vagaries which had plagued him since he first began his research on narcotics.

Based on the fact that, in the previous nine months, some thirty-five kilos were intercepted, the official estimated "about ten times more got through."

"How do you arrive at that?" asked David.

"I don't know. Maybe we're catching only one per cent instead of ten per cent. I guess the honest answer is, I don't know."

David had brief interviews with a few senators who were serving on an international opium control committee and came away with the only solid conviction of the past few weeks—that the only way to solve the nation's narcotics problem was to dry up the source. The United Nations was working on that. David returned to New York with a brief case full of pamphlets, speeches and facts.

Back in his apartment, he opened up the small console table to its full length and spread out all his material—notebooks, pamphlets, books, photographs, speeches, envelope jottings—on the top. Then he drew up a sketchy outline, separating the material under five basic heads: first was a general introductory piece, including some of the history of narcotics; second, narcotics and schools; third, a visit to the city's institution for addicts under twenty-one; fourth, medical opinions; fifth, opinions at the nation's capital, the federal difficulty, the U.N. action.

David put his coat and hat on, went out and took the uptown subway to the *Ledger.* Once again sitting opposite Holloway, he told him what he had gleaned. He mentioned the wide variation of opinion which existed in almost every facet of the problem.

"Well if that's what it is, there's no help for it," commented Holloway. "What have you planned?"

"I think it can be done in five articles," David told him, and outlined what he intended to cover in each.

"Sounds all right," said Holloway. "How soon can you have them?"

"The end of the week?" queried David. Today was Tuesday.

"Oh, you can have till the middle of next week. I want the first article to begin on a Sunday. Good luck." He offered his hand in farewell.

David stopped by Alice's desk on the way out.

"Can you get away for coffee?" he asked.

"I think so," she answered. "You go on up, and I'll see you there in a minute or so."

Over coffee, the two discussed the series. "You have all your information now?" Alice asked.

"I certainly hope so," replied David fervently. "Any more and I think my head would split. Do you have any idea of the ramifications of this thing? It's not only local—it's national and international. The sick, shaking addicts I've seen in court and in hospitals have their counterparts all over the world—what a mess!"

"Well," comforted Alice, "it's all over now but the writing."

"What do you mean 'but'? That's the toughest part of the job!"

"Not once you get started," predicted Alice. "You'll see."

She was right. It took David almost two hours to get started, but once he did, it just kept rolling. He had the five articles written by Friday, but edited them down three times before he was satisfied that, within the limits he had set for himself, none of the vital points had been omitted.

Wednesday morning, he dropped the copy off on Holloway's desk and then went downtown to the Criminal Courts building.

In Friday's *Ledger,* there was a small box at the bottom of page one, announcing that a five-part series on the nation's narcotic problem, written by David White, would begin in the *Ledger* on Sunday. The same box appeared on Saturday.

When David picked up the fat Sunday paper, he felt it had been worth it. At the left top of the page, in the off-lead position was:

THE NATION'S NARCOTIC PROBLEM
Tragedy of Addiction Centers on Adolescents;
Its Prevention Is Hampered by Disagreements
by David White

David went to the phone and dialed Alice at home.

"How would you like to have lunch with me?" he asked, exuberantly. "Let's wallow in luxury—I feel wonderful and I want to order caviar and truffles! Does that sound like a sensible lunch?"

"Oh, Davey—don't be a dope!" Alice laughed.

"Don't ever say that word to me!"

☆☆☆ *38*

VIVA MEXICO!

THE NARCOTICS SERIES was very well received. A number of prominent people who were active in the problems of narcotic addiction wrote the *Ledger,* complimenting the paper on performing a public service by offering such a series. Many others wrote, commenting on the clarity and presentation of the extremely difficult subject. And, while there always are a few people who will read articles composed of hundreds of thoroughly documented facts, only to pounce on one minor inaccuracy—not a single carping letter was received.

David was glad it was all over. Two publishing houses, devoted to the printing of specialized literature for students, asked him to write a narcotics chapter for their books. The fee was nominal—but since David had most of the facts in his head, the only nuisance was the typing, so he consented. Once he put those into the mail, a weight was off his shoulders.

A few weeks after the final article had appeared, Holloway beckoned him over. "How'd you like to go to Mexico?" he asked abruptly.

"Narcotics?" asked David apprehensively.

Holloway laughed. "No—a junket. Our travel editor, poor man, can't take two junkets at once, much as he'd like to. And right now he's in South America. You've been working pretty hard and the Mexican sun ought to do you some good—even if it is only two days. Want to go?"

David gulped. "Love to! You sure you want me to have it?"

In reply, Holloway handed him a telegram which consisted of a formal invitation. "Call them up and tell them you're going for the *Ledger*. All the details are on there. Have a good time. Adios, Señor." He turned away and busied himself with some papers. Basically a shy man, Holly was embarrassed at a show of gratitude and hid his feelings behind a show of gruffness.

"Thanks very much," said David quietly and walked off with the lengthy telegram.

Roger Mulvaney didn't seem to be doing much, and David approached him, telegram in hand.

"Roger, I don't know much about junkets. Can you fill me in?"

Mulvaney glanced over the telegram and pursed his lips. "I guess you're the fair-haired boy today," he said, impressed. "You know, the city room rarely gets a smell of these. The travel editor, the aviation editor and a very few others who play it close to the vest have cornered the market. They travel to every interesting place in the world—in style and for free. That's what a junket is. When a luxurious new hotel opens in Siam, or a steamship company launches a new billion-dollar vessel, or—as in your case—a domestic airline has just gotten a franchise to fly non-stop to Mexico—why, a maiden voyage is launched, on which the press is invited. They are under obligation to do nothing but enjoy themselves—and, of course, tell their millions of readers what fun it was!"

Mulvaney's voice had an edge which softened somewhat as he added, "I'm glad one of these finally seeped into the city room. On the really big jaunts, the brass goes. It's rarely that a working stiff gets a smell of these."

Something Mulvaney had said bothered David. "You mentioned writing a story about it—Holly didn't say anything about a story!"

"Then don't worry about it," counseled the rewrite man. "It'll probably be taken care of in advance, and then in a straight news piece on the day the run is open to the public. You go call them up and tell them you're going. They'll take care of the details—they're the best detail-take-carers-of you've ever known." He laughed. "You'll get such service and such attention you won't be fit to live with for a week after you get back!"

David dutifully telephoned the offices of the East-State Airlines and told them he would represent the *Ledger* on the trip. Within an hour, he received a telegram from the airline. Fortunately, he had been talking with Alice and was still in the city room when it arrived.

We are very pleased that it is possible for you to join us on our pre-inaugural flight to Mexico City this Thursday. We will board our flight at eleven a.m. and would appreciate it if you would check in with your baggage at our midtown office at 9:15 a.m., Thursday, where limousines will be waiting to take you to the airport. It will also be necessary to bring along proof of citizenship, such as birth certificate or passport. My office will contact you shortly to obtain some brief information for a tourist card for you which must be presented in Mexico in order to obtain entrance into the country. We will secure this card for you and it will be given to you on the airplane. If there are any other questions, please do not hesitate to call this office.

David had luckily brought his birth certificate to New York and he had it readily available. He got a smallpox vaccination from a doctor with an office in the *Ledger* building. The injection took a couple of seconds and was painless.

The night before he left, he had dinner with Alice. He was almost too excited to eat. Alice wasn't overly-hungry either. "Can't you smuggle me along?" she asked wistfully. "I'm green with envy."

David was suddenly contrite. "I'm sorry, Alice," he said. "I'm just so tickled to be going, I didn't think." He paused a moment. "Boy—wouldn't it be wonderful if you could go? What a time we'd have! What shall I bring back for you? What would you like?"

Alice smiled. "Oh, any little old thing—a hacienda, say. Or maybe a barrel of silver. Some such insignificant token. After all, it's the thought that counts!" They laughed, but she refused to be pinned down, insisting, "I'd rather be surprised."

After he took Alice home, David checked his suitcase for the ninth time. He was to spend three nights and two days in Mexico. In his bag he put a suit, slacks, four shirts (one was a synthetic with quick-drying propensities), underwear, pajamas, shoes, toilet articles. Just on a chance, he tossed in a pair of bathing trunks.

As he fell into bed, he thought, "Tomorrow night I'll sleep in Mexico!"

The next morning, in the company of some twenty-five persons, David stepped into a huge, new, four-engined silver plane, the interior of which was all gold and completely air-conditioned. The president of East-State Airlines, a famous man in aviation circles, was on board, surrounded by a coterie of airline publicity employees. Apart from the press, there were a few men in allied fields, such as the city's Marine and Aviation Department. With all that, the plane was about a third full. An East-State Airline man told David they would make stops in a few key cities on the way south, to pick up additional newspaper men.

The plane took off into a brilliant sun, and climbed quickly to a height of 20,000 feet, where it leveled off at a cruising speed of three hundred thirty miles an hour. The white clouds floated lazily by the window, like so much cotton batting, and the sun was a huge yellow ball in the sky.

This is the way to live, thought David, and gave himself up to the lovely haze of relaxation. A tap on the shoulder brought him to. An extremely pretty girl, the stewardess, asked him whether he would like some lunch and handed him a menu: fresh lobster cocktail, Rock Cornish hen on wild rice, vanilla ice cream with fresh strawberries—and champagne.

David enjoyed a gourmet's lunch.

At the stop in Washington, D.C., David was happy to see Michael Crosby, of the *Ledger's* Washington bureau, come aboard with others. Crosby had been quite helpful to David when he visited the nation's capital while gathering material for the narcotics series, and the two men greeted each other cordially.

There were a few other stops, and by the time they reached

New Orleans, the huge plane was full. There was an hour stopover in New Orleans, and David sent Alice a box of pralines from a sweet shop in the airport. It was hot and very sticky there and the passengers were happy to enter the air-conditioned comfort of the huge silver plane. Next stop: Mexico City!

David leaned back in his comfortable seat, put his feet up on the unusual triangular-shaped, foam rubber footrests, and relaxed.

Nine hours out of New York, the huge plane glided to a smooth stop at the ultra-modern airport at Mexico City. A number of natives in colorful national garb were part of the welcoming committee and provided gay music while the debarking took place.

David could only marvel at the dispatch with which everything was handled. Customs were a matter of minutes and a large bus was waiting to take the Americans to their hotels. Everybody had a private room, and the guests were divided between two of the best hotels in Mexico City. The airline was really spreading the carpet!

A mimeographed sheaf of papers was propped on the desk of David's room; it was a program covering the three nights and two days of the stay. That night, David noted, there was to be a cocktail party and dinner at a nearby hotel; Friday's agenda listed a visit to University City, lunch at a countryside villa, and return to Mexico City via Cuernavaca. A small footnote here stated, "Those guests who enjoy swimming and photography should not forget their swimming suits and cameras." On Saturday, there was special transportation to the Jockey Club, at Mexico's beautiful race track. Refreshments and lunch would be served at the club. Dinner was planned at a smart hotel (transportation provided) and, for this last evening of entertainment, the group would be joined by officials of Mexico and Mexico City. The final morning,

Sunday, listed departure instructions. They would be back in New York Sunday night.

The two days in Mexico were a happy haze of lavish living and magnificent color for David. His impressions included the overpoweringly beautiful buildings of University City, with the stunning stone mosaic murals, driving through the mountains at such heights that one drove literally through the clouds, the opulence of the race track club, the delightful swim at a beautiful outdoor hotel pool where they lunched one day, the shops, the sights—alas, David was homeward bound while he was still absorbing the warmth and exotic flavor of this magnificent land.

"How was it?" Holloway asked, when David reported to him on his return.

"I'll never be the same," replied David simply.

Holloway grinned. "You'll get over it. Those junkets spoil a man for regular living. Too much filet mignon, lobster and turkey—not to mention the native specialties. You had lunch yet?"

David grimaced. "I don't think I want to eat for a week!"

"You'll get over that, too." Holly laughed, and waved him off.

At dinner that night, David attempted to tell Alice about the incredible two days, but his impressions were too fresh—everything merged and blended and all that came out was, "You wouldn't believe it—it was so beautiful. What an exciting, magnificent country!"

"I can imagine," replied Alice, again wistfully.

David turned to her slowly. "Alice, we'll go there together one day, I promise you. Those two days just whetted my appetite. And all the time I was there, I kept thinking, 'If Alice were only here—what a bang she'd get out of it.' And then I knew that I'd come back—and you with me. We'll go there on our honeymoon!"

Alice fiddled with the giant silver earrings David had brought her and then looked up into the earnest brown eyes of her companion.

"David," she said with arch coyness, "what a way to propose!"

"Alice," said he impatiently, "stop acting like a girl!"

MILTON LEWIS

In the course of being interviewed by Milton Lewis, many criminal lawyers have interrupted the trenchant interrogation by protesting plaintively to their inquisitor, "I didn't know you were a lawyer!" He isn't, but it is a tribute to his wide knowledge of courtroom lore that he is frequently mistaken for one.

He is a member of that rare genus known as a native New Yorker—born, bred and educated here (with time out at the University of Wisconsin). Like David White, he also served his apprenticeship as copy boy (nights, while attending high school), and subsequently furthered his newspaper education as district reporter.

During World War II, Mr. Lewis served with the Eighth Air Force in England and Belgium, writing accounts of the fighter group to which he was attached as an enlisted man. After the war, he returned to the *New York Herald Tribune* as a general assignment reporter.

In that capacity he has covered many of the major happenings in the city, specializing in crime, and is a trusted confidante of many of New York's most respected jurists and public officials, as well as denizens of the underworld.

Mr. Lewis is married and the father of two children, Peter, 9, and Jane, 7, who are far more impressed with their daddy's ability to water ski than they are with his "business," probably because most projected leisure-time excursions hinge on the big "IF"—"if the office doesn't call."